BOOK ❷

WEIGHT-

THE NEGATIVE EFFECT

LOSS

OF BODY IMAGE ON

APOCALYPSE

THE HCG PROTOCOL

ROBIN PHIPPS WOODALL

NOTE: Women and men both experience hCG medical weight loss, but for convenience, we primarily used *she/her* throughout.

NOTE: To differentiate the original *Weight-Loss Apocalypse* from this edition, we will refer to the original as *Weight-Loss Apocalypse-1 (WLA-1)* and this edition as *Weight-Loss Apocalypse-2 (WLA-2)*.

<u>Dedication</u>

To Dr. ATW Simeons for his curious mind, his lifetime of scrupulous observation, and his steadfast belief that the body isn't as naïve as we think.

To the scientists who've dedicated thousands of hours exploring the curiosities and intricacies of the human mind and body—not because they want personal gain, but because they are seeking what is important to humanity.

To all of the people who've personally shared their hCG protocol experience with me on many levels. They opened up about the truth of their wins and losses, and the vulnerable truth of their struggles. It is their humility and willingness to be honest with me and with themselves that allowed the Mind:Body Method to evolve.

To the most important people in my life: My husband Mark and my children Chloe, Wyatt, and Suzanne. *You brighten and magnify the light of my soul with your unconditional love.* Thank you for believing in me, and for having patience during the years I couldn't find the energy, motivation, or discipline to get this work done.

Contents

SECTION 5
When Shame Threatens Your Survival

SECTION 6
Letting Go

Introduction

"I believe the hCG protocol is like a slap in the face. It can knock some sense into the reasons why we eat, and can help us recognize the magnitude of the consequences stemming from feasting before and after 'diet famine.'"
— *Weight-Loss Apocalypse-1*, chapter 13 page 137

My intentions and integrity when I wrote and published *Weight-Loss Apocalypse (WLA-1)* in 2011, was to start a conversation about modern science applied to Dr. Simeons' hCG protocol, and the potential environment it could provide to help address emotional eating. However, I knew as I continued to learn and evolve that at a later time, I would have to update the approach and further the discussion. Today, I feel ready to add to that original conversation.

Because my approach to Dr. Simeons' hCG protocol has evolved, I've spent a lot of time questioning whether I should re-write the original version of *WLA-1*. I chose to update some of the terminology in the book around "gluttony," and while encouraging the use of the rhythms of hunger and fullness to guide eating, I added content about using the protocol as an opportunity to quit all forms of dieting. For the most part, I left most of the content as it was originally written because I believe the information is an important step in understanding the bigger picture. The content of the original *WLA-1* still holds true. The science is the same, the hCG protocol hasn't changed, and eating to hunger still holds significance. But the approach to address emotional eating (with or without the hCG protocol) must be refocused as my awareness of the healing process expands and gets clearer.

I expect that my own understanding and growth will continue, and with that, this 2020 edition will be relatively insufficient in the future. I apologize ahead of time for what I don't know that *I don't know yet!* As I work with increasing numbers of people, and the issues become more and more predictable, I will continue to improve my own discernment and nature of the issues, as well as improve my ability to explain it in a way that is easily understood. That doesn't mean what I'm writing in this edition of *Weight-Loss Apocalypse (WLA-2)* doesn't have importance— but that we still have so much to learn. My goal in writing this current edition of *WLA-2* is to share what I've learned since 2011, and to go deeper into the problem of emotional eating. I want to take the discussion about cultural gluttony that I focused on in *WLA-1* to the next underlying levels.

In this edition of *WLA-2*, I will:
- Try to help people wanting to do the hCG protocol for the first time to better assess if they are an appropriate candidate for it.
- Help people who have done the hCG protocol, but have struggled to do it successfully, to understand why.
- Reiterate that the hCG protocol is *not a diet*, but a medical therapy, and address the emotional and psychological risks and downsides of the hCG protocol when it is approached like a diet.
- Clarify why I believe the hCG protocol can be a dangerous trigger for some people to possibly develop disordered eating and eating disorders, and how the protocol is attractive to people who already suffer from those issues.
- Expand the discussion about emotional eating to what is underlying and promoting it.

- Explain how I prepare people for the hCG protocol with this updated approach.

This edition of *Weight-Loss Apocalypse-2* isn't about weight loss, it isn't about the *hunger scale*, and it certainly isn't about cultural gluttony. It's about opening your mind to look at why you battle weight, and to recognize the limitation and constraints this battle imposes on your life, with food, with your body, and with your desire for belonging.

If at the end of this book you have a better understanding about the relationship between the negative perceptions about your body and your struggles with food,
then I have accomplished my goal.

SECTION I

HCG Protocol or HCG Diet?

A 40-year-old woman tells her story:

"Hi Robin, I've been following your YouTube videos for a while now and feel as if you're someone I can really talk to. But now I have reached a point in my life where I'm at my wits end. I began the hCG protocol a year ago and lost about 35 pound over several rounds. The reason for this is because I will complete a round, complete the three-week stabilization; then end up gaining back anywhere from 10–15 pounds in the maintenance phase because I go on bingeing/purging or just bingeing sprees. So, to compensate for the weight gain, I'd do another round of hCG."

"I'm getting so obsessive over my weight and so emotionally drained from all the dieting that I have now developed an anxiety disorder and have had frequent panic attacks over it. I feel that I am ALWAYS on the hCG diet and cannot enjoy my life for fear of gaining the weight back. I've avoided social situations where I know there will be food and/or drinking present, so instead of enjoying my life, I shut myself in. Other times when I allow myself to indulge, I completely go on an all-out bingeing spree and I feel horrible about myself shortly after. I used to binge and purge, but

5

now I've gotten past the purging and just end up bingeing and living with the discomfort after."

"Sometimes I feel as if the hCG diet was the best and worst thing that ever happened to me. At first it allowed me to lose weight and lose weight quickly. But after the stabilization period is over at every round, I feel as if when I add back in the "normal" foods, it causes me to gain weight so easily that it frustrates me. Then I give up and go back to old eating habits (bingeing, or just unhealthy eating). I get depressed about the weight I have put back on and go on another round of hCG like I mentioned before, and it drains me and frustrates me. Currently I am on (hopefully!!) my last round of hCG. I'm in the stabilization period on day 11. I really, really, really, do not want to go into that "dark place" again by bingeing and gaining the weight back, and definitely DO NOT want to do another round of hCG."

"I would really love to have my sanity back again and stop worrying and being so obsessive about my weight. I realize that I've been rambling and I apologize for that, but I feel that you, being experienced in hCG protocol and eating disorders would have more understanding of these kinds of things. Watching your YouTube videos I often thought to myself, "If only I lived in her area, I would love to talk to her. She really seems to 'get it.'" I realize you must be very busy but I would greatly appreciate any words of advice or even if you could recommend a colleague in your field that lives in the Southern California area that I may consult with, preferably with your similar expertise (fat chance I know but it's worth asking). Any words are greatly and tremendously appreciated."

Chapter I

What I've Learned After *Weight-Loss Apocalypse*

> *"Relearning to trust the physical cues of hunger requires that you let go of calorie counting, pre-portion controlled foods, and pre-determined meal times. It demands that you end all emotional judgment about food. You must completely start over with your diet so you can develop confidence in your ability to listen to your body when eating—without the extreme opposites of our cultural excess, and without a diet's control."*
> – Weight-Loss Apocalypse-1, chapter 3 page 28

One of the most difficult aspects of preparing people for the hCG protocol is educating them on how it works. In 2010, when I worked at a medical hCG weight-loss clinic before publishing the original *Weight-Loss Apocalypse (WLA-1)*, clinic staff would spend at least two hours introducing people to a basic concept of the protocol before we felt that they were informed enough to decide *if it was something they were willing to commit to*. We also spent between three to five hours preparing new patients before they started the protocol. This was taking far too much time for people at the clinic—and new patients had to absorb and remember an overwhelming amount of information.

I wrote *WLA-1* to provide a way to reduce the amount of energy and time those overseeing the hCG process spent making sure people understood what they were signing up for *before starting the protocol*. We needed to condense the preparation time from four hours to two, not only benefitting the potential client, but our time efficiency at the clinic. The book allows the potential client to learn at her own pace, giving her adequate time to understand the process.

After publishing *WLA-1*, the goal was to have people read the book before coming into the clinic. This would eliminate people who weren't serious about the 500-calorie protocol—and it would allow those who were serious a way to understand the process, and thus come to our clinic prepared with questions more personal to their situation that we could answer. We wanted them to recognize, for themselves, whether they were or were not a good candidate for the process.

I also knew it wasn't realistic to expect everyone to buy and read *Weight-Loss Apocalypse-1*, so we found another solution to help people understand the protocol ahead of time: record a short video as I explained how the hCG prevented starvation, and why the 500-calorie protocol is necessary. That video was imbedded on the homepage of the medical clinic's website, along with a link to purchase the book. These things made our efforts to educate and prepare people significantly easier—and the people coming into the clinic were far more excited, less fearful, and more committed to the process.

See video: *https://www.youtube.com/watch?v=xiqs4MDFQ2w*

We also wanted people inquiring about the hCG protocol to understand how the process can impact them emotionally. I recorded a session with a new patient as I prepared her for just that.

See video: *https://www.youtube.com/watch?v=G1AeDwT0tOw*

The book made a positive impact at the clinic where I worked, but it has also helped numerous other medical clinics across the country. Since publishing *Weight-Loss Apocalypse-1*, I've been contacted by doctors, practitioners, therapists, coaches, and medical clinics regarding their successful use and implementation of the book to prepare patients in their program.

People who were attempting the protocol without the aid or assistance of a clinic also provided feedback. They found that *WLA-1* helped them get a better grasp of *why* and *how* the protocol worked, and how seriously the protocol should be taken. But what helped them the most were the sessions I posted on YouTube. The most feedback is related to these videos and recorded sessions (accessible to the public) because they gain expanded insight into the application of the hunger and fullness scale and the hCG protocol. The recorded sessions have allowed people to see the Mind:Body HCG Method in action, as described in *Weight-Loss Apocalypse-1*.

So far, I now have over 800 FREE YouTube videos of sessions with clients who are working through the process, and today, they are all available to the public. But as I've improved my capacity to teach and understand the process, the content of these sessions has naturally evolved.

What *Weight-Loss Apocalypse-1* Was Missing

One of the biggest issues with *WLA-1* is that it doesn't go in-depth into *why people eat emotionally*, and it doesn't offer a solution—but rather it provides a discussion about the problem. I knew I didn't provide in-depth solutions or discussion about why people eat emotionally because *WLA-1* was not written as a self-help book.

Above and beyond the main goal to educate and help patients and practitioners prescribing the hCG protocol, my intent was to discuss the possibilities of the protocol, with more research and observation. I saw the potential of the protocol being used as a tool to help people address and recover from both the psychological triggers and the physical consequences of excessive over-eating.

When *WLA-1* was published I knew, at some point, I would have to address emotional eating, but I didn't want to discuss it until I had grasped a bigger picture of the problem.

The book does provide a basic way to identify emotional eating with the application of the hunger and fullness scale, but it doesn't go far beyond that. One reason is that I didn't then adequately understand the complexity of the issue, and I knew I wasn't practiced enough to write about it with confidence.

I understood:
- The excess weight people thought was the problem, was actually a symptom of the problem.
- People had a "disconnect" when discerning real physical hunger from emotional hunger, and from emotional wants and needs.

> *However, what I didn't fully grasp enough to write about then was the degree that people emotionalized their need to lose weight, which put a direct strain on their relationship with food.*

Even though I made the connection that weight loss shouldn't be the reason or the reward for eating to hunger, and that people shouldn't weigh themselves during the process, I didn't completely understand the impact that negative body image had on the outcome of emotional eating, and the difficulty that impact would have on people's discernment and ability to listen to hunger. Boy, was I naive! I am addressing this big hole in the content of *WLA-1* in this new *WLA-2* edition.

As the diet industry continues to say that people overeat because of the pleasure they get from food, or from the components/additives, etc. that food contains, they aren't addressing or questioning people's emotional issues with body image.

> *People aren't seeing emotional eating as a consequence*
> *of the stigma and shame people hold about their size and*
> *weight, and how that promotes anxiety and fear with food.*

As I've continued to work with hundreds of people, observing their reasoning for dieting and their resulting strain with food, I see a common theme throughout. It isn't about the food, nor is it common that a traumatic past caused it. Surprisingly, for most people it is simpler than that.

> *It's about what they get out of being thinner—*
> *and as a result, the feelings of disconnection*
> *and shame for being fatter.*

What's New with *Weight-Loss Apocalypse?*

Since publishing *Weight-Loss Apocalypse-1* almost a decade ago, I have monitored over a thousand rounds of Dr. Simeons' hCG protocol done by patients seeking to address emotional eating with the Mind:Body HCG Method. I introduced this Method as an approach to Dr. Simeons' hCG protocol as a platform for participants to identify and address emotional eating.

The objectives of the Method were to:
1. Identify stages of physical satiation or complete fullness.
2. Identify states of physical hunger.
3. Differentiate mental hunger from physical hunger.
4. Identify triggers that prompt mental hunger and emotionally validate eating.
5. Allow discomfort without justification or action.

6. Eat based on physical need, reconditioning functional eating in any uncontrolled situations.

A full description of this Method and each objective appears in chapter 11 of the original *WLA-1 and again in Section Five of this book.* I introduced the use of the hunger and fullness scale to regulate food consumption, alongside the very low-calorie protocol. Since then I have been able to apply this Method and observe how people responded to 1) food restriction, 2) perceptions of deprivation, and 3) their weight. As I've monitored more and more people, recurring problems have become predictable patterns that have allowed me to evolve and improve the Method.

The focus in the first edition was on the hCG protocol, eating by the body's guidance, using the hunger and fullness scale, and from there, to address emotional struggles people had while working through the process. The main focus was the physical aspects of the method, and with time—as I've refined my understanding and ability to communicate the fundamental issues with emotional eating—my energy has shifted toward the "Mind" of the method, or the emotional side of the process.

One of the most important improvements I've made as a coach and teacher of this method is my specific understanding of how perceptions and negative body image influences how people respond to the *hunger and fullness scale—* which is a physical aspect of the method to describe the physical sense of hunger, satiation, and fullness (see below).

The idea described in *WLA-1* is based on the science of leptin, which is a master hormone that coordinates the increase and decrease of hunger. The hunger and fullness scale can be used as a conscious reference to understand leptin levels, as well as when the need to eat food is hormonally appropriate.

- The hunger and fullness scale helps people verbalize and discern the physical sensations that the body signals to guide when and how much to eat.

- Recognizing the sensations of physical hunger and fullness allows the participant to learn the difference between her body's physical need for food and her emotional desires to eat.
- Having an awareness of the difference between physical hunger and emotional hunger is an imperative step towards understanding the root beliefs and thoughts that promote the desire to eat when there is no hunger, or to eat beyond comfortable satiation.

This is the basis for the Mind:Body HCG Method described in the original *WLA-1*.

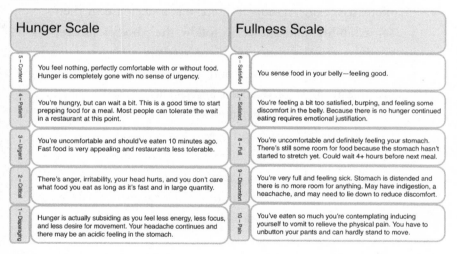

Hunger Scale		Fullness Scale	
5 – Content	You feel nothing, perfectly comfortable with or without food. Hunger is completely gone with no sense of urgency.	6 – Satisfied	You sense food in your belly—feeling good.
4 – Patient	You're hungry, but can wait a bit. This is a good time to start prepping food for a meal. Most people can tolerate the wait in a restaurant at this point.	7 – Satisfied	You're feeling a bit too satisfied, burping, and feeling some discomfort in the belly. Because there is no hunger continued eating requires emotional justifiation.
3 – Urgent	You're uncomfortable and should've eaten 10 minutes ago. Fast food is very appealing and restaurants less tolerable.	8 – Full	You're uncomfortable and definitely feeling your stomach. There's still some room for food because the stomach hasn't started to stretch yet. Could wait 4+ hours before next meal.
2 – Critical	There's anger, irritability, your head hurts, and you don't care what food you eat as long as it's fast and in large quantity.	9 – Discomfort	You're very full and feeling sick. Stomach is distended and there is no more room for anything. May have indigestion, a heachache, and may need to lie down to reduce discomfort.
1 – Disparaging	Hunger is actually subsiding as you feel less energy, less focus, and less desire for movement. Your headache continues and there may be an acidic feeling in the stomach.	10 – Pain	You've eaten so much you're contemplating inducing yourself to vomit to relieve the physical pain. You have to unbutton your pants and can hardly stand to move.

When Weight Interferes with the Hunger and Fullness Scale

I received a lot of positive feedback about the science and application of the hunger and fullness scale presented in *Weight-Loss Apocalypse-1*. Overall, people felt hope and confidence that the concept of following hunger and fullness as a guide to when, and how much one should eat, would relieve them from having their mind so focused on restricting. Readers were intrigued by the notion that the body could do the job of directing food intake, and this made them hopeful that they wouldn't have to rely on memorizing diets the rest of their life, just to maintain their weight.

But as I continued to implement this approach to Dr. Simeons' hCG protocol, I started seeing predictable trends. We observed that how people felt in regard to following the physical guide of hunger and fullness to regulate food intake, *dramatically changed* before, during, and after they lost weight on the very low-calorie protocol. They would adjust their willingness to rely on their body's hunger rhythms to guide them, depending on how important their weight was.

- No matter how refined, accurate, and aware they become of fullness and hunger, fear of weight gain negated their willingness to follow it.
- When people's emotions and strictness about their weight increased, understandably there was a decrease in their sense, ability, and choice to follow their body's hunger rhythms—*in fact, they were afraid to follow it.*
- Underlying strain with their body and their desire to be, and stay thinner, promoted anxiety and fear about food—which fostered a difficult, and often impossible environment for them to relax in order to learn and discern hunger and fullness.
- As people's feeling about their weight grew more and more negative and their fear of weight gain more intense, the anticipation of increased food restrictions promoted significant increases in food intake.

The link between body image, fear of food, and difficulty eating to hunger became increasingly more obvious as I worked with more and more people—to the point where I could predictably sense when a person was going to struggle based on the degree of emotional strain she had with her weight and size.

For some people, it wasn't fear of weight gain, but emotional excitement about successful weight loss that promoted a desire to eat beyond fullness—as if they were giving themselves a reward. The end goal of eating, based on the biological rhythm of hunger and fullness described and promoted in *WLA-1*, became irrelevant the more emotional that participants were about being thinner, losing weight, and keeping off the weight they lost. However, when people were indifferent about weight loss or weight gain, *eating to hunger* came naturally.

This made the Mind:Body HCG Method approach in *WLA-1* appropriate *only* when people weren't emotionally charged about weight loss, weight-loss maintenance, and weight gain. Consequently, my approach to teaching the hunger and fullness scale as a way to work on emotional eating had to be adapted.

I found that 1) by initially prioritizing and addressing body image, then 2) adequately practicing *eating based on the body's rhythms of hunger* before starting the protocol, there was a radically reduced likelihood that the participant would revert back to old patterns of emotional eating when the process was over. This gave the healing benefits of the protocol a chance to work after she had transitioned back into eating a large variety of food as she would in the real world without being controlled by a diet.

Before starting Dr. Simeons' hCG protocol:
  – We needed to understand why, and to what degree, the client was emotional about her weight and body fat.
  – The emotional charge driving the desire to lose weight needed to diminish.
  – Then, as fear-based, diet-induced stress around food relaxed, her priority became learning the sensations of hunger and fullness, as described in *Weight-Loss Apocalypse-1*.
  – From there, we could more clearly address relationships with eating that were developed as emotional coping mechanisms.

The "Mind" of the method needed to be addressed first, then second, the "Body" of the method. As a client's underlying emotional strain with body fat and her emotional charge to be thinner was resolved, fear about food diminished, and she had an easier time discerning and relying on hunger.

15

It was only then that *eating to hunger* felt more relaxed and natural as described in *WLA-1*.

These additions and adjustments to the order of the Mind:Body HCG Method approach added more time and preparation before participants started Dr. Simeons' hCG protocol. For many people, it took well over a month, sometimes two to three months, before we could focus on the hunger and fullness scale. For some people it takes years.

As a participant understands within herself how important emotional recovery is to her body's physical rehabilitation, she recognizes there are risks if she rushes too quickly into the very low-calorie protocol without having done the necessary emotional work. She sees that what isn't addressed ahead of time will have to be addressed afterward, and afterward the issues will show up as emotional urges to overeat.

**If a person wants to help the body heal, she needs
to resolve the underlying issues before attempting
the healing process of the hCG protocol.**

With this awareness, participants are less impulsive to start the protocol—they want more time to practice eating freely without the pressure to lose weight and the anxiety or tension of food restrictions. I've had clients who, after experiencing the ease and freedom around food without the stain and pressure of dieting, chose not to do Dr. Simeons' hCG protocol. They chose to accept their body as it was, in order to free themselves from the torment of the all-or-nothing pendulum swing between dieting and overeating.

I do not believe the protocol is necessary for people to free themselves from emotional eating, and to learn to eat without the controls of a diet. The truth is, for many people the hCG protocol is another restrictive diet that triggers emotional eating. For them, it is best to do the Mind:Body Method without Dr. Simeons' hCG protocol.

To free yourself from the strain you have between dieting and your desires to overeat, you must address the negative strain you have with your body as it relates to body fat. Once that is addressed and resolved, only then can the complicated relationship you have with food relax.

Chapter 2

Does the HCG Protocol Work?

"The reason why I created the Mind:Body HCG Method was to help expose participants to a functional approach to eating and a revolutionary way to use Dr. Simeons' protocol for that cause. The goal is to approach Dr. Simeons' hCG protocol not as another diet, but as a tool to help redefine emotional self-esteem that's not reliant on eating, and that's not enabled by another diet."
— Weight-Loss Apocalypse-1, chapter 11 page 112

If you've ever done the hCG protocol as it was written by Dr. ATW Simeons, you know it works. Of course, you lost weight. Of course, you lost inches. But when someone who has never attempted the hCG protocol asks someone who has done it multiple times if it works, and that person recalls the unique challenges each round brings to the 500-calorie protocol, the answer is not a simple "yes."

When I'm asked if the hCG protocol works, the first thing that goes through my mind is this: I must figure out exactly what I'm being asked. There are many facets of how the protocol works, and its complicated to give a simple yes or no answer.

- Do people lose a pound of fat a day? *It depends.*
- Is the hCG effective to make the 500-calorie protocol sufficient to prevent starvation and too much hunger? *It depends.*
- Can the protocol improve metabolic rates? *It depends.*
- What about people's cravings and emotional eating; does the protocol make these impulses go away? *It depends.*

Will the hCG protocol work for this person who's asking if "it works?" Only if he or she is willing to do it as it is prescribed, even under pressure, stress, and environmental change. No one can predict this. In most cases, the protocol works as it should—as long as the person doing it makes his or her eating lifestyle adapt. But even then, the body must adapt to internal and external environmental change.

Most people believe that by following the 500-calorie protocol as described by Dr. Simeons in his manuscript, *Pounds and Inches,* that the protocol will magically work perfectly. They believe that being perfect in the restrictive food intake is what maximizes the potential healing process the protocol holds. But from years of observation, I've concluded that the protocol's specific food limitations *are only part of a large equation.* I believe that both the participant's physical environment and her emotional temperament are equally important factors.

How Changing Physical Environments Affect the Protocol

The protocol works well if it is followed as prescribed. But as soon as there are large environmental shifts creating inconsistency, the body must adapt to maintain hormonal balance, and that adaptation can speed up or slow down the metabolic process. Think of it like a car that must accelerate or decelerate to stay on a winding road that bends and goes up and down hill. As you go up hill, you need to put your foot on the gas pedal to stay the same speed. To stay the same speed when driving downhill, you might have to put on the breaks to a certain degree. And to get around a sharp corner, you'll have to slow down. The body responds similarly to environmental shifts on or off the hCG protocol, speeding up or slowing down to maintain hormonal balance.

If the protocol is done 1) as prescribed with an effective hCG prescription, 2) adequate pre-loading or forced feeding prior to starting the very low-calorie protocol, 3) earnest effort to eat what is prescribed, and is eaten to the biological rhythm of hunger, the protocol should effectively keep the body in a steady range of hormonal balance. And as described in *Weight-Loss Apocalypse-1,* the body shouldn't mimic the typical hormonal response to starvation that the 500-calorie protocol would without hCG.

But that alone doesn't guarantee optimum metabolic and fat-loss results. For example, 1) things as natural as hormonal shifts that occur during a woman's menstrual cycle, 2) when flying to a destination where the weather patterns are different, or 3) when a person gets more or less sun exposure than usual, can challenge the metabolic hormonal balance during the very low-calorie protocol.

Although many people face challenges adhering to the food restrictions of Dr. Simeons' protocol, sometimes the challenge is environmental shifts not necessarily in the control of the participant, like challenging sleep patterns. I've had many clients who worked night shifts, but not consistently. I make sure they know ahead of time that inconsistent sleep patterns will definitely impact how their body responds hormonally to the protocol.

Many of the clients I've worked with have needed to travel internationally for work or vacation while on the very low-calorie protocol. Some of them prepared enough to be able to follow the restrictions. Others needed to eat off protocol for fear that they would offend the hosts who prepared them food. But whether they followed the protocol perfectly or not, it was impossible for them to remove the stress on their sleeping rhythms and the extreme change in their physical environment traveling from one part of the world to another. Almost all clients I've observed on the protocol who've traveled extensively have physical reactions that counter what they typically experience when they are consistently in a more controlled environment.

No matter how controlled your physical environment is or isn't, the biggest vulnerability for almost all people attempting Dr. Simeons' hCG protocol is their emotional state of mind. The choice to follow the very low-calorie protocol is directly impacted by the participant's state of mind, but even with perfect adherence to the protocol, I've observed stress is equally as influential.

How Emotional States of Mind Affect the Protocol

Changes emotionally, physically, and environmentally that impact the hormonal (endocrine) system of the body can have a direct effect on the potential therapeutic benefits of the protocol. Many people restrict perfectly on the very low-calorie protocol, but because of environmental challenges that are out of their control, they don't get the stellar results they experienced with previous rounds—or what they would expect when eating such a severely restrictive amount of food. There are legitimate circumstances that promote fat preservation and less fat metabolism during the very low-calorie protocol, regardless of a person's physical potential for fat loss.

> **EXAMPLE:** One client experienced a series of incredibly stressful events while on the very low-calorie protocol. She ran a family farm and while on the protocol, they lost a large number of their livestock in a tragic accident where the animals suffocated to death. Not only did this impact her financially, but the sadness and loss of a couple hundred animals was traumatic, and they also had to retrieve and discard their bodies that showed signs of physical distress. This was like losing loved pets in a shocking and terrible way.

To add to her burden of grief and trauma, a couple weeks later her son's wife, who was pregnant with her first grandchild, was diagnosed with preeclampsia. This is when the pregnant mother's body experiences symptoms of toxicity, and her blood pressure goes up alarmingly. The risks can cause organ damage to the mother, and could be life threatening to both mother and baby.

This client's fear and stress of losing her daughter-in-law and first grandchild was made worse by the memory of her own traumatic loss of a baby. Despite her ability to stay on the protocol, the food limitations weren't enough to make up for the metabolic impact caused by the incredible degree of loss, grief, fear, and stress. Not only did her weight loss flatline, but she was so emotionally and physically stressed that she ended up with shingles and a flare-up of her rheumatoid arthritis.

In this case, the client did exactly what she was asked to do on the protocol, but her life stress could have promoted an inflammatory response that, when combined with the inflammatory side effect of the hCG, created a reaction the very low-calorie food restriction couldn't balance out. Under the circumstance, the best thing she could do was find ways to reduce the inflammation by addressing her grief, accepting the situation, and attempting to reduce her fear and resulting stress. Medication, counseling, meditation, talking about it, and getting rest were the best remedy at the time. Despite her desire to eat food out of feeling burdened and punished by her situation, she decided to stick to the protocol and learn to accept and emotionally adapt to the life experience.

Even if the protocol is followed as Dr. Simeons intended, while also incorporating the adapted use of eating to the biological rhythms of hunger as described in *Weight-Loss Apocalypse-1*, if the participant experiences high levels of stress, anxiety, or grief—the physical results will be impacted. Ideally, the client has a secure life that allows for a stable, at-ease state of mind.

Like this client's unpredictable circumstance, there are many factors, other than food and calorie-burning capacity, that influence the potential of the protocol. It's not that the protocol didn't work, but due to the severity of her stress, her body probably didn't respond the same way it would have if she was in a more stable emotional environment. She also might not have had as severe a physical reaction to stress, like getting shingles, had she not been injecting such a hormonally inflammatory amount of hCG. In many cases where the protocol doesn't seem to be working, it isn't that the body isn't adapting, but rather the participant is struggling to (and in many cases, can't) adapt their lives to access the metabolic potential of the protocol.

The Benefits of Consistency During the Protocol

The difficulty answering the question of whether the protocol works or not is that it's not a black-and-white question with a yes or no answer. There are many moving parts that have nothing to do with the hCG or the very low-calorie protocol. Even though the very low-calorie protocol is black and white in nature, the environmental and emotional influences that can impact the healing process are not. Therefore, the more consistent and stable all the dynamic environments are, the more healing potential the protocol might have to work with. The more change and environmental fluctuations involved, the healing potential of the protocol shrinks.

In scientific terms, the protocol's potential would be maximized if the participant is kept in a "vacuum." This means being isolated from temperature change, pressure change, and elevation change, and the participant is placed in a perfectly controlled cocoon without movement, activity, or even consciousness. We'd have to remove perceptions, thoughts, and anything that would create fluctuations in this person's emotions that might add more inflammation. Relative to complete and total stability, the protocol's physical

24

benefits are more stable the more predictable that people's emotional and physical environment are. Unless they are in a coma, none of this is possible, and of course it isn't ethical.

In reality, to get the most out of Dr. Simeons' hCG protocol, the participant will need to do the best he or she can to create as much consistency physically, environmentally, and emotionally as possible. This is done all while living busy lives with changing schedules, travel, caring for children, meeting the demand of their jobs, and with endless dynamic change to their sleep, temperature, menstrual cycles, weather, activity, and what we call "life." And when their life is always unstable, the goal would be that their protocol expectations allow for and accept how that way of living impacts their end results. Even if they create stability during the very low-calorie protocol, if the true nature of their life is chaotic, they will return to that way of being, and the results will adapt and adjust back to that reality.

When Adherence to the 500-Calorie Protocol is the Challenge

Outside of the physiological needs for the protocol to work (hCG, loading, food restriction adherence), the most important aspect of the protocol is the participant's motivation and willingness to follow the protocol, no matter what environmental change she experiences.

Although it might seem that the constraints of the food on the protocol is the most important, it actually is how the participant responds emotionally to those constraints, in different environments. This is because she must be willing to stick to the very low-calorie protocol as best she can, in order to allow the protocol the space to work. If a person feels restricted, bored, and punished because she doesn't have the same freedom to eat like she used to, she is less likely to stick to the protocol, or more likely to demand more weight loss than is realistic for her body. The protocol can seem easy to follow in situations that don't require sacrifice, but it can seem punishing when a situation makes it very clear that you aren't allowed to eat food the way you are used to.

EXAMPLE: One day the food on the protocol is easy to manage. You went to work prepared, pre-weighed the meat, put the measured veggies, fruit, and cracker servings in a box-like plastic container. You get hungry...you eat. The next day you do the same exact thing, but your car gets a flat tire on your way to work. You get to work late and missed a very important meeting, and now don't have the same amount of time for a lunch break. A co-worker brings in delicious-smelling pizza and a birthday cake to share.

Ask yourself:

- ☐ Under this type of stress, and surrounded by the sights and smells of food that isn't on the protocol, would you find it more difficult to stay in the boundaries of the protocol?
- ☐ Would it feel like a cruel form of punishment?

Most people would say "yes."

To some people, the protocol limits are too restrictive and demanding when she feels like she is withheld from experiencing the ease of their normal eating behavior. The difference between the freedom she normally has about the way she wants to eat, from within the limits and boundaries of the protocol, can promote feelings of being withheld or deprived of available food, even when she isn't hungry or physically having any problems. And if she is hungry, protocol food she prepared can seem worse than it truly is when compared to flavorful food others are eating around her. In the end, how people position themselves within the protocol boundaries, in any given environment, determines if the person is willing to remain within those food constraints.

Compare what it takes to do the hCG protocol to what it takes to drive a car. If the car has gas and all parts function, the car can drive. But can the person behind the wheel drive the car? Sure. Can that person adjust to driving in a mountain range without road signs, or a speedometer? Do they know how to accelerate and decelerate to remain safe on a curvy highway? That takes practice and focus.

It isn't the protocol that is the concern—it's the driver of that protocol that must be prepared for emotional and physical variability before attempting it.

In reality, what it takes emotionally to do the hCG protocol is not as simple as linear math, it's more like physics. It's takes the ability to drive through that mountain range with changing angles, directions, elevations, temperatures, oxygen levels, and pressure gradients. It requires the ability to not only adjust one's seat position and internal car temperature in order to be comfortable, but to also maneuver and adapt to the rise, fall, and turns with the appropriate car speed to not tumble down the mountain side. And sometimes the protocol feels like a steep mountain you just can't get around, but as long as the participant is adapting to that environment, the process of the protocol will work. However, it might not work the way you want it to.

When It Takes Thought and Preparation

It takes legitimate sacrifice in order to follow the protocol as it was intended, and for the body to respond accordingly. However, how a person feels about that sacrifice ahead of time while she fantasizes about the weight loss, might be completely different than how she feels as she must sacrifice food in that moment.

Ask yourself:
- ☐ Are you willing to sacrifice the simple ease of not having to think about what you can and cannot eat?
- ☐ Are you willing to measure and weigh appropriately from a select choice of protein?
- ☐ Are you going to be able to adapt to social functions where

food and alcohol is being served that you cannot eat or drink while on the hCG protocol?

☐ If you get a gift of cookies from a friend, will you be able to accept them without eating them?

☐ How would you feel if you follow the protocol and make sacrifices socially with food, but don't lose the amount of weight you think you deserve?

Participants have many reasons to deviate from the restrictions. However, over the past ten years as I monitored and observed people make multiple attempts and rounds of the hCG protocol, this is what I learned: *The most influential roadblock is the participant's expectations and reasons for doing it, and this makes the biggest impact on how she or he performs.*

When it is approached like a diet, predominantly motivated by emotional needs to lose weight, and less as a medical therapy for long-term physiological healing, there is psychological and emotional strain that creates stress during the process that conflicts with the entire curative purpose of the protocol.

I believe all people doing the hCG protocol bring to it emotional wants and needs, otherwise she wouldn't be driven to do it. Whether it's an emotional decision based on changing the way she looks, or based on how she perceives her health, the degree to which she emotionalizes the results is where I've observed conflict and problems involved with following the very low-calorie protocol.

In the end, the more emotional a person is about her needs and expectations for the results of the process, the more the protocol *is a diet rather than a medical hormonal therapy.*

Chapter 3

Why the "HCG Diet" Doesn't Work

"If after the protocol, you're willing to let your body control when and how much you eat, no matter how vulnerable you feel, you've won the battle—physically and emotionally."
— *Weight-Loss Apocalypse-1*, chapter 5 page 70

There's always an awkward moment after someone asks me what I do for a living. I'm not sure what to tell them, and I'm not sure they'll understand. Usually I try to avoid bringing the hCG protocol into the conversation and simply answer that I help people with emotional eating and body-image issues. But if they pry further, inevitably my book, *Weight-Loss Apocalypse-1* and the hCG protocol comes up in the conversation, and that's when the focus on the work that I do goes deeper than I'd like it.

Discussing the hCG protocol is complicated, and understandably, most people's first reaction to it is with skepticism and judgment. Most are initially surprised that I'm associated with the hCG protocol, especially since my primary work is helping people recover with body-image issues. It seems counter-intuitive to also be supportive of such a controversial and radically restrictive process. When people hear I'm an advocate of Dr. Simeons' hCG protocol, their curiosity end ups pushing more conversation.

They often say, "I know this one lady who did it a few years ago, and she lost a lot of weight. But she's gained it all back, and I don't see her out much anymore. I know another woman who seems to be on it year-round. She's doing it every time I talk to her. The diet is extreme, right?" People's first assumption is that *the hCG protocol is a radical scam diet for crazy people.* Often, I have a hard time not agreeing with them. In many respects, their assumptions are true—especially when the protocol is approached like any other diet.

The general view of the hCG protocol is that the long-term health benefits are unrealistic and unachievable. Many people who've done it would say the same thing, especially after doing it over and over again, and finding it almost impossible to manage the weight loss when the protocol is over.

> **IMPORTANT:** *There's a difference between Dr. Simeons' hCG protocol done as a medical treatment for hormonal and metabolic problems, and the hCG protocol done as an impulsive diet solution for weight loss.*

The truth is, even when approached as a medical therapy, the hCG protocol is radical, and it can be dangerous to the mind and body of those who inappropriately attempt it.

However, I've also been contacted numerous times by people who've had miraculous experience with the hCG protocol.

- They lost a large amount of weight, some people losing over 100 and 200 pounds.
- They no longer needed certain medications.
- Previous symptoms like hot flashes, heartburn, sleep apnea, or low energy went away.
- They were able to sustain these benefits for multiple years.

But at some point, as they thought they needed to lose more weight, they attempted more rounds of the hCG protocol than they should have, and their successful results went away over time. Unfortunately, they became miserably obsessed with their weight loss, their food intake, and dieting as emotional eating and binge eating returned. And some even resort to abusing diuretics, cleanses, and even purge their food like a bulimic, in order to avoid regaining weight. In the end, most people find they begin to have more disordered eating behaviors after having done the "hCG diet" over and over again. Ultimately, any significant amount of fat loss returns—and so does shame for not being able to maintain those losses.

The Shame of Regaining Weight After Successfully Losing Weight on the HCG Protocol

Over the last ten years while observing people of all walks of life attempt the hCG protocol, I've witnessed that the more emotional someone is about his or her weight, the more difficulty is experienced during and after the hCG protocol. People not only magnify the psychological importance of the fat loss during the protocol, but they experience magnified fear of fat gain when it's over. Regrettably, the fear of regaining the weight they lost impacts how participants relate to food in such a way that they experience anxiety and paranoia about food, and they become fearful to eat when the very low-calorie protocol is over.

If they inflate themselves with pride when they lose weight during the protocol, their pride backfires, showing itself as exaggerated fear of weight gain when the protocol is over. And ultimately, pride turns into extreme shame when they gain weight back after it's all said and done. This fear of weight gain is projected onto food, as if food is the enemy and is the threat to pride, and as a result people seek extreme controls and restrictions from food after the protocol. This fear promotes a need for strictness and perfectionism, and their approach to restrict food tends to be unrealistic—often requiring them to isolate themselves from social engagement. As a result, the urge to eat emotionally intensifies and people find there's an emotional all-or-nothing swing between under- and overeating.

31

Strict Dieting After the hCG Protocol

Truthfully, did the protocol work to improve the function of the metabolic system, if in order to maintain fat lost, the person needs to continue extreme diets that necessitate radical restriction? Should a person have to restrict sugar, dairy, gluten, grain, starchy fruits and vegetables, and have to exercise excessively for the rest of his life just to maintain a stable weight? With that type of stringent focus and life dedication to maintain the end weight, clearly the participant *is not open to the protocol as hormonal therapy,* but rather he is fixated on how weight loss benefits him emotionally.

Ask yourself:
- ☐ Would you need to continue such modes of starvation if the hCG protocol "reset" your hypothalamus (part of your brain), as Dr. Simeons has described?
- ☐ If you have to go to such reaches to maintain body fat, did the protocol correct your lagging metabolism?

The answer to both is "No!"

> **In order to fully understand the real impact the hCG protocol has on the body, it's imperative that fears and other emotions attached to weight gain and weight loss are addressed and resolved ahead of time.**

The Benefits of First-Round Skepticism and Low Expectations

In the beginning, before a person commits to her first round of the hCG protocol, she keeps her personal hopes about weight loss a good distance away from her expectations as she studies the protocol from both a medical treatment as well as hormonal and metabolic-therapy point of view.

There are concerns with injecting pregnancy hormones, starvation, micro-managing the seriousness of the very low-calorie protocol, and anticipating, with an open and curious mind, what Dr. Simeons' described in his manuscript, *Pounds and Inches.*

- Will the hCG hormone sufficiently remove hunger so that 500 calories of food feel satisfactory?
- Are metabolic and hormonal issues stemming from large amounts of body fat started in the hypothalamus of the brain? This is the control center of the brain that regulates many of the body's hormonal mechanisms.
- Could the shape of the body change, and other endocrine issues be resolved when the hCG protocol is given adequate time to work?

Even when people are terrified by the prospects of the protocol, there are enough ways to relate to what Dr. Simeons' describes as a hypothalamic disease that people feel a sense of hope.

The protocol seems too good to be true, but the way Dr. Simeons describes 1) three types of fat, 2) where abnormal fat accumulates, 3) how difficult it is to lose weight in these areas even when in starvation, but 4) how with pregnancy the fat redistribute, is too relatable for people to ignore. Dr. Simeons' medical approach gives reason why diets have always failed, and gives people hope that there is a possible solution for excess body fat and metabolic problems, but not enough for them to naively jump into it with full confidence.

It's too radical for people to blindly get overly excited when the outcome isn't a clear guarantee—especially for people who've been dieting for decades, and who've *experienced far more failure than success.* Particularly since people are taking a huge leap of faith in the hCG protocol when there is no scientific evidence, updated laboratory or clinical studies, and without the support of the FDA. (This is discussed in Chapters 6 through 8 of *WLA-1.*)

The internet contains a lot of support and information, which can give people a sense of hope and possibility. However, before they know if it works or not, people don't invest all of their emotional needs into it when they don't feel safe or trust the reliability and forgivability of process. They have to complete the protocol in its entirety for themselves, before they emotionally commit.

For most people, that's how they relate to their first round of Dr. Simeons' protocol—with healthy skepticism. Their approach is serious, a bit unconvinced, yet hopeful. They are open minded to results of the protocol, following it as best as possible to give it a chance as a hormonal and physiological process. Because most people's first round of the hCG protocol is taken seriously, studied, and strictly followed as it is medically prescribed, most feel content with it. Typically, hunger is manageable, and as Dr. Simeons describes, people lose a surprising amount of weight, with dramatic size loss. Many people also experience great relief from other physical symptoms that, previously, they thought were impossible to remove.

During their first round, as people's confidence in their ability to follow the restrictions of the protocol increases, and they witness the physical results, their stress and insecurity with it naturally reduces. People get into a rhythm with the process, especially if they have no major life crises that throw them emotionally and physically off-course. Once people get into the groove, they often describe the protocol as relatively easy, especially when they physically feel markedly better.

With past diets, they got used to working extra hard, having to go against the grain, and push through hunger, cravings, and feelings of deprivation for very little reward. Even if they find the protocol challenging to follow, if they do what it requires, the results are significantly magnified compared to what they are regularly used to. This gives them a sense of hope going into the second (or exiting) phase of the protocol.

As people transition into the second phase where the hCG hormone is removed and food is strictly and strategically reintroduced, most people continue

34

to witness the protocol's healing potential, and often feel incredible gratitude and awe for their body. They are relieved, elated, and hopeful for long-term results. But for others the vulnerability of regaining weight without the safety and control of the very low-calorie protocol can feel scary, and some people become even more unsettled and untrusting about their newfound leaner body.

As Confidence Rises, Expectations Rise Too

No matter how successful a person might have been their first round of the protocol, there are certain changes that happen the second time they do the protocol that make it much less effective and harder to follow. I've observed that as people feel confident that the protocol works as a reliable way to lose weight, they become more critical and less forgiving of their body fat.

In general, as most people experience such poor results over and over again with previous attempts to lose weight, they eventually come to lower their expectations with their weight-loss goals. But after experiencing such rapid and dramatic results with the hCG protocol, their expectations rise, inadvertently creating a more negative outlook and attitude about their current weight. Before the protocol, their extra weight was tolerable, after losing twenty to thirty pounds, the smaller amount of extra weight they still have *is less tolerable.* After the protocol, they're less gratified than they thought they'd be after successfully losing weight. Once the goal is achieved, expectations rise, and their appreciation is diminished.

Even after losing a sizable amount of weight, as a person continues to be unsettled about her body fat, this changes how she feels about doing the protocol again, and what she expects in weight loss as a result.

This translates to wanting physical change—but for psychological benefits. The protocol is no longer a medical hormonal treatment, but instead it's used to serve emotional struggles that people attach to their weight.

Emotional Expectations and the "hCG Diet"

As people's confidence in the reliability and weight-loss results of the protocol increases, and their discontent with their body remains, it is at this point they feel safe and comfortable bringing their emotional goals to the forefront of why they're doing the protocol—*and that changes everything.* The specific method and particulars of the protocol doesn't change, but the person's context, intention, and expectations for the protocol changes. She approaches her next round of the hCG protocol more like the "hCG diet," and for this reason, she doesn't think of it or follow it the same way.

When done as a temporary medical therapy, the limitations of the protocol are impersonal, just as impersonal as having to drink nasty liquid to clean out your system for a colonoscopy. With medical procedures, the expectations are hopeful but not guaranteed, which keeps people open and unattached to the results. Similar to a colonoscopy, you don't demand a specific reward just because you spent most of the night needing to use the toilet. You hope to learn something, which is how the hCG protocol was intended to be approached. But as soon as it's made into an emotionally motivated diet, the restrictions become personal, and so do the results.

In short, the hCG protocol is a medical treatment for long-term physical healing, and when it's done to gratify immediate emotional needs, it becomes the "hCG diet."

When the motivation moves towards being emotional, people project all sorts of fantasies, hopes, needs, and wants into what they expect to get out of the results of the protocol. It's as if losing weight is the key to their survival—as well as the gatekeeper to happiness and freedom in life. Consequently, there is a profound straining effect on how people approach the limitations of the very low-calorie protocol.

The more emotionally important the weight-loss reward becomes, the stress around the food restrictions get more intense. As the strain between the protocol restrictions and their weight-loss results becomes more pressur-ized, people tend to weigh and measure their body to check the results—some do it over five times a day.

Simply explained, *when the protocol is done as an impulse to gratify emotional needs for weight loss,* the expectations are intensified and pressurized, which distorts how people respond to the restrictions as well as the results. It changes to not being as black and white as Dr. Simeons intended, where the participant adapts to the process for the body's physical needs. Instead the participant complicates the process by adapting the protocol to meet his or her emotional needs.

This takes away the open-mindedness and relaxed curiosity about the results people experienced during their first round, and instead promotes a drive and intensity that tries to force a specific result.

SECTION 2

When It's Easier to *Not* Follow the Protocol

Request for Robin's help:

"I'm 49 years old, and I've been trying to maintain a skinny body—and have managed to successfully control my weight (by all unorthodox means necessary)—for most of these 30 years. However, since being introduced to the hCG protocol three years ago, concerns about my weight have become downright stressful. With hCG, I finally lost those 20 pounds, but I keep going on and off the protocol. I can't tell you how many times I've done the protocol over the last three years. Now that I'm five days into Phase 3, I had a meltdown and am starting hCG again. Why? I overindulged on pistachios, and I feel like a failure and I have to start again. Clearly, I have a problem...I need help."

Request for Robin's help:

"I did the protocol May of 2017 with success, but didn't do it for the right reasons, and gained the weight back. I have been to several psychologists over the years, and none of them have helped at all. After watching some of Robin's videos, I truly believe she can help me learn why I do what I do."

Request for Robin's help:

"Two years ago I did the original hCG protocol and lost 32 kilos (about 70 pounds). But I was stupid enough to do 21-day rounds, with only two weeks maintenance between...back-to-back for five months. Doing it this way was extreme, but I felt amazing the closer I got to my goal. Then I stopped, my hair fell out, and an insatiable unearthly hunger came over me, and I ate like I had been starved until I reached my original weight. The hunger was so bizarre and unnatural that I was waking up in the night to eat."

"Summary since then: many failed attempts to redo hCG, complete inability to stick to any plan whatsoever, and the sort of depression that comes from huge regret and anger at myself, and the humiliation that comes from a small-town environment where everyone saw me lose; then gain it all back."

"I have huge shame attached to this, and have avoided going out socially and even spending time with my family. I binge at home thinking that I'm going to start the protocol again, but I can't bring myself to follow through. So I've gotten larger than I have ever been. Help!"

Chapter 4

The Strain Between Weight Loss and the Protocol

"Whether you've gained two hundred or ten pounds of fat because of dieting and resultant emotional eating, to eat functionally you have to listen to hunger, eat when it's present, and stop when it subsides."
— *Weight-Loss Apocalypse-1*, chapter 3 page 49

When people think about their desire to lose weight, they rarely base motivation on the physiological advantages. Even if a doctor or scientists observing the process thinks about it from a hormonal or medical vantage point, the participant rarely thinks that logically or intellectually about weight loss.

For most people, their perception of body fat is totally emotional. Body fat is symbolized as an indication of failure, weakness, exclusion, social rejection, laziness, illness, inadequacy, abandonment, isolation, and lack of love in their life.

Some important emotional facts:
— People often attach emotions of sadness, anger, and embarrassment to the way they perceive their body in relation to their size and weight.

41

- On the other hand, people also attach positive symbolism to weight loss.
- The idea of being leaner and thinner often is symbolized with hard work, determination, education, will power, acceptance, approval, health, achievement, success, and worth.
- The emotional attachment that people commonly associate to weight loss is love, pride, confidence, security, safety, and freedom.
- For many people, weight loss is also associated with feelings of anxiety, pressure, perfectionism, isolation, paranoia, and fear of regaining the weight.

When someone wants to do the protocol, especially for the second, third, fourth or fifth time, more than likely his or her main motivation isn't physiological at all, but rather the incentive is primarily driven to remove the negative symbolism and emotions attached to fatness, and wanting to gain the positive symbolisms and emotions that are attached to being thinner.

These symbolic reasons are why people are emotionally driven to diet, and this can make a significant impact on how people become attracted to doing something as extreme as the hCG protocol. It also can impact how they assess whether the effort, sacrifice, and strain to restrict is worth the reward.

**The more emotionally rewarding the weight loss is,
the less people are realistic about their ability
to follow the protocol food restrictions.**

When Fantasy Expectations Make the Protocol Seem Easy

When deciding if the protocol would be worth it, the sacrifice it takes to restrict yourself from the normal way you eat is compared to the emotional reward of losing weight. With this, people aren't necessarily aligning motivation with the hormonal and physiological aspects that the hCG protocol was intended for—and this can undermine the consistent adherence a successful protocol requires. They underestimate how difficult and strenuous following the protocol will actually be.

> **Example:** If someone wants to lose thirty pounds in order to feel confident enough to put pictures on a dating website, she will assume the rewards of fat loss will make a positive impact on her sense of worth, safety from rejection, and her sexual attractiveness. Depending on the degree to which that person needs and wants to develop a relationship, the results of the protocol would supply a huge emotional value. This magnified emotional bias and need for weight loss inadvertently minimizes the perception of the degree of difficulty people expect from the 500-calorie restrictions. *Their desperation for connection and companionship makes the strictness of the protocol seem worth it.*

In essence, they are basing their motivation and predicting their ability to restrict food on emotional desires that in no way correlates to their body's physiological need for food. How people relate to their body doesn't necessarily align with how they relate to food—especially when the desire for food is as dynamic as the time of day, the social environment, the sight, smell, and availability of food that is in front of them—or as variable as the situations for which they've developed an emotional need for food as a coping mechanism. The moment they are hungry, bored, feeling deprived, and are separated from family and cultural connectivity through food, or when they want to eat for some other emotional need, their evaluation of their ability to restrict (based on the value of weight loss) is far more difficult and confusing than they anticipated.

I've commonly observed that when people visualize the value of the protocol based on the emotional impact weight loss provides, they are not realistically looking at the strain of the protocol restrictions. They combine the best-case scenario in terms of the ease of restriction to the best-case scenario in terms of the weight-loss result, which sets them up to feel overly strained and victimized by the restrictive process. They didn't anticipate the influence of stress, work, kids, loss, gain, celebration, anger, boredom, loneliness, exaggerated hunger from premenstrual symptoms, and social events where food will be abundant. *Their naive expectations that it would be easy isn't questioned or looked at as the source of their frustration with the protocol.*

> **EXAMPLE:** One client described a day where she experienced a flat tire, a sick child at home that needed tending to, a project she couldn't finish, and a complaint from a neighbor about her barking dog. She was so proud that she didn't cheat that day, but when she woke up and weighed herself the next morning, she was totally disappointed. She was expecting to lose at least a pound, maybe two, but the scale showed a loss of only a half a pound. She not only felt discouraged, but angry.
>
> She went through the entire day, sacrificing the food she felt she deserved because of her troubles that day, thinking she would be greatly rewarded with extra weight loss. Not seeing those losses, she felt victimized by her prior stressful day, but also victimized by the protocol. As a way to feel better about it, she spent that entire day deviating from the protocol and bingeing on food she felt she deserved to eat, knowing that the next day she'd fix it all by following the protocol perfectly. This was a common reason for deviating from the protocol that we saw with almost every single patient at the hCG clinic.

When the Protocol is Followed, but With No Weight-Loss Reward

One of the hardest factors is when a person does sacrifice the ease of eating without food restrictions in order to adapt to the protocol, but it doesn't reward her with the weight loss she feels she deserved. The goal is that no matter what the body does, the participant is willing to adapt to the limitations of the protocol, without feeling punished, victimized, and deprived, even if the body loses fat at a rate slower than expected. In this case, the weight-loss expectation is the most influential factor as to whether or not the protocol is working.

Getting participants to have realistic expectations, and to accept the truth of their body's results, is the most difficult task when preparing them for Dr. Simeons' hCG protocol.

Despite the actual physiology that is working perfectly on the protocol, if weight isn't lost at the rate one expects in his or her head, their adherence to the limits of the protocol might not continue.

It's not uncommon for a person to "eat off the protocol" the day she wakes up and doesn't see anticipated weight loss. What can make her feel worse is if the previous day felt stressful, and the protocol felt more sacrificial, more restrictive, and more emotionally demanding than she thought it should. In that case, if her next-day's weight loss doesn't reflect a loss that feels equal to her sacrifice, the protocol can feel punishing. *People feel that because they adhered to the protocol while under stress, they deserve more weight loss.*

Unfortunately, this emotionally diet-minded approach to the protocol gives her a one-sided expectation, both emotionally and physically. This sets her up to be victimized, disappointed, and discouraged by the limitations of the protocol as well as the fluctuations that are a normal part of the weight-loss aspects of the process. Because the restrictions are more difficult than she anticipated, the demand for sufficient weight loss increases.

Emotional "Apple Day": This emotional response to the protocol and its results are why I believe Dr. Simeons added both the apple day and steak day to the protocol. Even though physiologically they do nothing significant to the rate of fat metabolism, these weight-stall breaking days are a way to distract the participant from her discouragement, and to provide a sense of immediate control and hope for weight loss and what feels like emotional success. Inappropriately, the apple and steak days that Dr. Simeons described in his manuscript, *Pounds and Inches*, only exaggerate, enable, and placate the short-term emotional impulses and expectations for fat loss. Rather than promote the long-term metabolic and hormonal impact that the hCG protocol potentially provides and was intended for, weight-stall breaking techniques diminish the profound purpose Dr. Simeons observed it to be.

Even if a person didn't break the protocol limitations, using the apple day or steak day can be an indication that the weight-loss results aren't what she expected, and also are not providing the emotional reward she believes she deserves.

She might be experiencing a life stress that normally would be coped with by eating. Because she chose to follow the protocol, her need for the weight-loss reward magnifies. Even if she lost weight, if the amount she lost doesn't match her emotional sacrifice from restricting food, she is likely to feel disappointed, frustrated, punished—or that the protocol isn't working. For this reason, she'll do an "apple day" to manipulate the scale so she feels adequately rewarded.

I do not recommend any form of weight-stall breaking methods and this includes the "apple day" and "steak day" that Dr. Simeons recommended.

How Emotional Stress Effects Weight-Loss Expectations

Patients that experienced stress, didn't cheat, and felt they deserved more weight loss because of it, predictably would call our office, concerned that the protocol wasn't working. A person would come to the clinic disappointed with her losses, complaining that she was experiencing hunger, and projecting her anger at us *as if we were:* 1) causing her stress, 2) punishing her, 3) withholding her food, and 4) were the cause of her anger. Understanding how that works, we'd ask about her stress levels at home, at work, in her family, and in her mind. We'd explain how that might increase her desire to eat, how that increases the feelings of restriction on the protocol, and how that in turn creates her greater demand for more weight loss.

EXAMPLE: When There Are Consistent Symptoms of PMS
Both men and women commonly describe symptoms that sound like pre-menstrual symptoms (PMS). Typical descriptions are: short-tempered, emotionally feeling they have a shorter fuse before they blow up, sensitivity to agitation, irritability, or feeling annoyed, and even feelings of sadness, loss, or being in the dumps. Whether it's actually a symptom caused by how the hCG mimics certain hormones, if it's a possible increase in testosterone, or if the participant is feeling emotionally stressed about the protocol limitations, many people justify eating food that's off the protocol because of their irritability. Or they eat more protocol food, because they think it is deserved because the protocol is punishing. This type of irritability often increased the participant's demand for more rapid weight loss.

The agitation, frustration, irritability, and sometimes anger that a person experiences when experiencing life stress, and she isn't rewarded with the weight loss she feels entitled to, can complicate her motivation to continue restricting on the protocol.

Even when she doesn't have physical hunger, when her emotional desire to eat increases and weight doesn't reduce as she expected, feelings of victimization are common and are predictable reasons people deviate from the 500-calorie protocol.

Most people hold the idea that the body should reward them in weight loss that's measured equally to the degree of sacrifice they made by not eating when and what they wanted emotionally. For example, if they feel their sacrifice of food on a scale of 1–10 was a 10 in sacrifice, then they will expect an equal 10 on a scale of 1–10 in terms of fat loss. This might translate to expecting a three-pound loss instead of a normally experienced half-pound loss.

Clearly the expectation isn't formulated based on science, physiology, or metabolic reason, but rather the person is exaggerating her need for weight loss based on her perception of deprivation and sacrifice. I believe this *emotional magnification of expected results* is not something a person is consciously aware she is doing. When she wakes up the next day and doesn't receive her expected weight-loss reward, the frustration is often expressed physically with an increase in cravings or the desire to eat. *People often think they are hungry, when in fact they are feeling emotionally deprived.*

When Disappointing Weight Loss Increases Your Hunger

When a protocol participant complains to me about cravings and perceived hunger, the first question I'd ask is if the cravings went up after she weighed herself, and if she was disappointed with the number. More often than not, this was the case. It wasn't hunger that went up, but her motivation to follow the protocol had gone down. It wasn't an increase in hunger, but rather an increased desire to eat emotionally, as well as a sense of deprivation.

> **EXAMPLE:** One woman came into the hCG protocol clinic where I worked and was very upset that she was hungrier, and she was concerned that the hCG wasn't working. After questioning her situation, we helped her realize it wasn't hunger, but her sense of feeling punished by the protocol limitations when a co-worker had brought birthday cake into the office. Because she refrained from the cake, she expected her weight to drop even more than usual. When it didn't go down as much as she felt entitled, her sense of wanting to eat immediately went up. She admitted that because of her frustration, she deviated from the protocol the next morning. *It wasn't true hunger that went up, but her feelings of punishment and entitlement to weight loss.* Naturally as she compensated herself with food not on the protocol, her body immediately stopped losing weight, making the situation worse in her mind.

Even if the protocol is easy for you, without continuous weight loss, your perception of the protocol is *that it is hard,* and compared to the abundance of food we have all around us, staying within the boundaries of the very low-calorie protocol is punishing.

Deprived of Social Engagement or Deprived of Food

If participants refrain from attending get-togethers, social engagement, parties, cultural rituals with food, or any instance where food is a symbolic part of culture, they wouldn't have much angst with the protocol restrictions. But they might feel disconnected from friends, isolated from life, and deprived of fun and people. On the other hand, as soon as they are exposed to others eating freely and who have open access to food around them, feelings of relative deprivation with food can set in, *even if they aren't hungry.*

> **EXAMPLE:** People get caught off guard with feelings of deprivation when they're on the protocol during a cultural celebration or holiday. When preparing to do the hCG protocol, and recognizing that they will be on the very low-calorie phase during a holiday, ahead of a time they often think that it won't be such a big deal, especially if they are losing weight. But when they are smelling the roasting turkey, the celery and onion frying in butter for the stuffing, their mother's homemade yeast-raised butter rolls, and the cinnamon pecan pie, the protocol restrictions might feel more complicated and depriving than they previously assumed. This is true especially if a person thinks she's lost enough weight to reward herself, or if she thinks she hasn't lost enough weight to make it worth the sacrifice of not eating at a celebratory feast.

When Confidence in the Protocol Increases Emotional Eating

A person who followed her first round of the very low-calorie protocol strictly and perfectly—because of skepticism as well as an honest effort to find out if it works—will find the protocol much harder to follow when that skepticism is gone. As her certainty and confidence in the protocol rises, she might become more lenient with the restrictions, as that confidence gives her a sense of freedom to "cheat" the protocol to see if she can still succeed in weight loss.

> **It's as if the participant is trying to find a "win-win" situation where she can lose weight without having to follow the protocol as it was intended. Because a person thinks the protocol is a guarantee to "fix" weight gain, emotional eating or overeating is justified, despite the fact she is deviating from the protocol.**

Sometimes people deviate from the protocol because they lose more weight than they anticipated, as if the extra fat loss entitles them to an allowance of extra food. It's as if they have extra credit, and that gives them permission to indulge, and have the room to stop losing weight—despite the hormonal ramifications that indulgence might cause.

When Weight Loss Affords You Freedom to Eat Emotionally

Some people that have clear and obvious physical limitation and ailments directly related to excess body fat *are rationally aware* of these physical issues. However, what she might be distorted and unaware about is with the severity and degree she is reliant on food and eating to handle emotional stress in her life. She might not consciously understand that her motivation to lose weight is to give her more time and freedom to emotionally eat, without the guilt of weight gain. In her mind, weight loss gives her room to gain weight.

Emotional eating has been minimized as a problem because it is a positive need in how some people handle boredom, social anxiety, fear of the future, resentments from the past, etc.

A person might have legitimate fears and concerns about the state of her body, and might be willing to temporarily suspend her emotional needs for food in order to alleviate these issues. However, as soon as she's lost enough weight to diffuse her physical concerns, she's likely to go back to her previous emotional relationship with eating to cope with hardships in life.

Losing weight gives her a sense of safety to eat emotionally. And for some, the perceived need to eat to cope with stress changes the outlook on her body, so that physical ailments and limitations are minimized and are less problematic than they truthfully are. Because she doesn't feel she can handle life without eating emotionally, she minimizes the significance of her weight gain in order to reduce the tension and pressure to diet. In addition, when she believes she can lose the weight again with a future diet, her emotional needs for food become the highest priority.

Undereating Followed by Overeating Followed by Undereating, etc.

Eating off protocol can create a long stall in weight loss, more than most people expect, making her feel an increased pressure to make up the difference or restrict more intensely to get "back on track." Not only does she think she has to get back to her previous weight loss if she gained weight from when she deviated, but it might take three to five days of strict protocol adherence for the scale to show losses again. It can be extremely disheartening for someone who felt emotionally high from the weight-loss success of the protocol to find that after a day of eating emotionally, free from the restrictions, that *the protocol typically works only with consistent adherence.* What she thought might take a day to recover from actually takes over a week.

When There's Weight Loss Despite Consistent Deviation from the Protocol

There's always that person you run into in a chatroom, on a YouTube video, or a friend who tells you she doesn't follow the protocol...and still loses weight. Usually when someone tells you this, it might be to suggest that you, too, can eat off the protocol, and you too will still experience daily fat loss. Unfortunately, her willingness to deviate from the protocol, and the weight loss she is telling you about, doesn't mean she is having a successful protocol. The reasons are four-fold:

1. Scale weight isn't necessarily a measure of fat weight. Her losses might not actually be 100 percent fat.
2. Her deviation might not have the same effect on her metabolism as it would on others' metabolic response.
3. The fact that she is consistently cheating on the protocol is

an indication of emotional strain with the restrictions and how it directly impacts the expected results with her body. She might not be losing as much weight as she is suggesting, but rather she has relaxed the expectations around fat loss in order to relax the strictness of the protocol.

4. The emotional lenience she is giving herself with food will not translate well when she goes back to life without any boundaries or restrictions.

Her emotional need to eat will still be there after the protocol. Any size and fat loss she does experience will definitely be regained after the protocol is over.

Too often people think that if they have a good reason to cheat, then the body should honor that good reason by not gaining weight or stalling their weight loss. It's as if the valid argument for why they deserve the food can change how the body responds physiologically to that food. We'd have clients come into the clinic disappointed they didn't lose any weight, even though they consistently ate off the protocol. They gave us excuses for deviating off the protocol, as if having reasons made it okay, and the body should have rewarded them with weight loss anyway.

When There's a History of Resentments for Having to Diet

For many people, years of chronic dieting bring to the protocol their feelings of emotional hardship with their body and a history of resentments for having been deprived over and over again.

Old grudges, like having to control or limit food as a child, are projected onto the diet. Consequently, no matter how promising and healing the protocol is physically, the resentment for having to restrict in order to receive another's approval, makes the protocol seem like a weapon or a sick form of punishment.

When the protocol is done to lose weight in order to gain another's approval, it is easy to feel deprived— and cheating is a foreseeable form of self-defense, retribution, and retaliation, even though it hurts only the body the participant is trying to fix.

And once the participant starts deviating from the protocol, she often makes it an all-or-nothing ordeal. The next thing she knows, she's completely quit a few days or a couple weeks into her protocol, thinking the next round will be easier.

She starts cheating, and creates her own modified version of the protocol— diminishing it from being a medical procedure to now, a lenient diet. And even if she follows the protocol to perfection, her feelings of deprivation and being punished in order to lose weight greatly diminishes her motivation to eat based on the physical sensation of hunger once the protocol is over. It's common for a person to think, "If I'm not going to lose weight this time, or am going to regain the weight, I might as well eat freely before going back to the restrictions later."

She often thinks that if she isn't going to lose weight, she might as well gain five more pounds, ten more pounds, or even twenty more pounds now that she knows the protocol is reliable, trustworthy, and can fix the weight gain at a different time.

Is the Problem the Protocol—or Is It Your Approach?

After a person experiences the miracle of her first round of the hCG protocol done as a medical procedure, she wonders why she can't stick to it and why it's become so hard. Despite the protocol's potential and physical promise, she doesn't recognize how making it about an emotional solution like with a typical diet, complicates and distorts the entire process. Once the protocol becomes the "hCG diet," it stops working—and so does the participant. I ask clients what they think would happen to their body's response to the hCG protocol if they were put into a coma. It's amazing to me that 100 percent of the time the clients inherently understand that the body works perfectly without them involved. But as soon as they consciously enter the picture, their perceptions and expectations cloud the process. The protocol becomes a desperate solution and a stressful diet that must be managed, as if the body won't work without their input and control. Their perception of their weight and of the food restrictions muddles the clarity of the process.

How could something so simple and so rewarding be so difficult? People think:
- Maybe it's the carbohydrates.
- Maybe they should add exercise.
- Maybe they should do a "clean" load where they force feed only on healthy foods.
- Maybe they should do a "ketogenic diet" when it's over, or intermittent fasting, or add more intense exercise.
- Maybe they should just stay on the very low-calorie protocol even when the hCG is gone.

Eventually, people start questioning if the protocol even works.

People start and stop, over and over again, wondering why the protocol is so difficult now when it was so easy before. Reality chews them up and spits them out bigger and heavier than they were. And for many, they end up with worse food issues than they had before. What changed? What was once hopeful and magical, now turns into an abusive, dysfunctional, and strained relationship with food and eating.

The entire concept of physical healing for the endocrine system is no longer in the picture. The qnce-relaxed and serious nature of the protocol as a medical therapy becomes a pressurized and hostile all-or-nothing diet.

Following the very low-calorie protocol feels like walking in a minefield full of food temptation. For this reason, diet businesses instruct people to stay away from social situations, and to avoid going out at all cost because the urge to cheat might be too strong. People are encouraged to fixate on their weight, with the assumption it will keep them motivated to stay on course, when in reality it causes more grief, resentment, and anxiety.

As the desire to eat increases, the need for weight and size loss becomes magnified in her mind, to the point where she fastidiously monitors her weight. It's common that an individual might weigh herself multiple times a day, body checking, and scrupulously tracking her shape with fanatical measures. We could always tell when a patient at the medical clinic was *emotionally strained* because she would measure her weight to the smallest value. Instead of rounding the number to the closest pound, she would manage each point to the decimal.

This type of emotional reactivity and impulsiveness is an indication of deeper problems, like an eating disorder, that the protocol might be exaggerating. A high level of emotional strain with the body projects a high level of strain onto the very low-calorie protocol, and puts a ton of emotional pressure on the weight-loss aspects of the diet—and this is an indication the participant isn't a good candidate for the protocol. *This begs the question then:*

Does the "hCG diet" work, especially when the participant is put into a position to manage every detail in order for her body to perform the way her emotions need it to? Is it worth it?

Chapter 5

False Advertising and Emotional Eating

"With a change in perspective, suddenly eating less doesn't feel punishing at all, and weighing yourself as motivation, seems stupid. This view changes what is perceived as emotional hardship—away from the superficiality of weight and emotional eating, to the profound and meaningful importance of life and family. Food instantly is viewed only as a physical necessity, and emotional eating is obviously viewed as irrational."
– *Weight-Loss Apocalypse-1*, chapter 4 page 53

When You're Given Unrealistic Expectations

Many times at the medical clinic, we turned people away from doing the hCG protocol. It's not that the person isn't capable, or doesn't have the physical need, but because she was not emotionally ready. However, we also had countless people come to the hCG protocol clinic thinking the 500-calorie protocol would be an appropriate means to lose five to ten extra "stubborn" pounds.

Sometimes we'd get calls from people attempting the protocol on their own, wondering why they are so hungry. We then learned that they were not even considered overweight, but were hoping to get down to a pair of size zero jeans. I've work with clients who were prescribed hCG by a physician, even when they clearly didn't have enough body fat to sustain the very low-calorie protocol.

Often when a person goes to a weight-loss clinic professing she has a problem, the medical team doesn't question the perception of the person paying for their services, even though she clearly isn't an appropriate candidate for the protocol's medical procedural restrictions. Nowadays, if you aren't ultra-athlete lean, you're considered overweight by cultural standards, and a weight-loss clinic isn't necessarily going to argue when they advertise you can achieve the same level of leanness with their program. In fact, their goal is to convince people to want and think the leaner size is achievable, and more clients will come in and pay for services at their clinic.

The more desperate a person is to be thinner, the more likely she will be attracted to something as radical and extreme as the hCG protocol.

We've worked with many men and women who wouldn't normally be attracted to something as radical, but they needed to lose weight rapidly for an important event like a wedding, vacation, or to meet physical requirements for an evaluation by the military. The more a person needs to lose weight "NOW," the more attracted she (or he) would be to the hCG protocol, especially if her exposure to it *is from advertising*.

When the "hCG diet" is promoted in the media, they use ultra-lean body images in their advertisements. That, combined with the idea that forty pounds could be lost in forty days, people with unrealistic expectations and anorexic-leaning disordered eating patterns are more likely to seek it out. It gratifies the best-case scenario for their impulsive desire to control food, and their emotional desire to be thinner. This makes it very attractive to people with more severe emotional issues with body image.

These images of ultra-lean people in ads feature pictures of someone who shouldn't have done the hCG protocol in the first place.

> **The emphasized body image portrayed doesn't show the excess skin or stretchmarks left over after losing weight you'd expect to see on a body that originally was appropriate to sustain the very low-calorie restrictions of the hCG protocol.**

The hCG diet industry has capitalized on Dr. Simeons' claims, selling it as if it's realistic for everyone, no matter what's your size. Even if you think you have only twenty pounds to lose, the claims make it seem as if you, too, will lose a pound of fat a day—which is completely misleading. This instantly promotes a dysfunctional purpose for the hCG protocol, as they are selling the protocol *as an emotional solution for weight loss rather than a medical treatment.*

These weight-focused expectations reflect the best-case scenario physically and emotionally requiring that most people live in isolation from life, or live life in a "vacuum," completely removed from reality. And even then, their assumptions don't include the truth of their metabolism, which for most people is radically different than what is reflected in advertisements. They might base their entire motivation to do the protocol on false advertising, which promotes the idea that it's normal for everyone *to lose forty pounds of fat in forty days.*

Consequently, people assume that if they lose that much weight so quickly, the sacrifice it takes to restrict food to the 500-calorie protocol for that long would be worth it. They are using unrealistic and incorrect rewards to determine the risk.

People derive their perceived ability to adhere to the very low-calorie limitations based on an outcome that is far from reality. They are set up ahead of time to struggle with the protocol when they don't lose that much weight.

Like the payoff at your work, if you were to work 80 hours a week and get paid $5,000, it might be worth it, but to work the same 80 hours a week and get paid only $1,000 when you were told to expect $5,000, would feel disappointing. Unrealistic expectations set a person up to experience relative deprivation, even when her body's physical response to the very low-calorie protocol is still dramatic.

> **EXAMPLE:** One client described how she normally would lose a pound a week with regular food restriction. On the hCG protocol she lost an average of three pounds a week. But because she was expecting seven pounds of fat lost per week, three pounds seemed slow, and she thought the protocol wasn't working, even though she lost three times the amount of fat more than what she previously experienced.

A person doesn't appreciate what the hCG protocol actually does for her physically—when she is set up to expect something completely unrealistic for her body.

Dr. Simeons discussed losing a pound a day, but his patients had enough body fat to be considered metabolically abnormal. I assume most of them were morbidly obese and in that case, many people do lose a pound of fat a day, and sometimes even more. It is more common to experience this dramatic fat loss for people who weigh well over two hundred pounds. The most I've witnessed a participant lose was close to two pounds a day. The man was over six-foot five-inches tall, and he weighed more than 350 pounds.

Even if a person has the weight, size, and metabolism to effectively burn an average of one pound of fat a day, if her motivation is purely emotional, she is more likely to cheat, and then she'll return to past dysfunctional eating patterns when the protocol is over. This negates the physical potential of the protocol—before she even starts.

Now that I've recognized this, and it has become clearly apparent, the process I take people through in preparation for the hCG protocol *is to first address their emotional needs,* as if weight loss is not their solution.

Put simply, when the person has too much emotional investment in the physical outcome of the protocol, she is not a good candidate for the hCG protocol. The less emotional she is about *the beginning and end physical result,* the better the candidate she is because she is less likely to underestimate the difficulty of the restrictions. This makes the medical treatment more pre-dictable if she is prepared to adhere to the very low-calorie protocol and the transitional restrictions as described by Dr. Simeons—allowing her body maximum potential for hormonal and metabolic healing.

If a person was told that realistically she'd lose only two to three pounds a week, or ten to fifteen pounds in that month, instead of thirty to forty pounds as advertised, she might not be disappointed so easily and then quit. And because the "hCG-diet" advertisements don't discuss other potential benefits of the protocol, people don't identify or give credit to improvements they experience in other ways.

> **EXAMPLE:** A person might experience more stable energy levels, more consistent and predictable menstrual cycles, improved sleep cycles, clearer skin, improved sex drive, more stable body temper-ature regulation, and overall mood improvement. The entire em-phasis on weight diminishes these important signs of endocrine improvements and meaningful benefits.

If these companies selling the hCG as a diet were truthful about how the protocol works, these are just some of the realities they would describe:

- Conclusive science behind Dr. Simeons' hCG protocol does not exist yet. Nothing is guaranteed.
- Don't expect to lose a pound of fat a day. The average participant will probably lose two to four pounds a week.
- You might lose between six to twenty-five pounds of fat during the very low-calorie protocol, and most people gain some weight back, even when they follow the protocol as prescribed.
- If you attempt the hCG protocol without having a metabolic problem or adequate fat to sustain hormonal balance, you will starve and experience all of the symptoms of starvation. Any weight you lose will immediately return.
- Some weeks the scale won't show you lost any weight at all, even though you are limiting your food consumption to around 500 calories a day.
- If you resume restricting and dieting again after the protocol, your body will continue to be metabolically sensitive to food, and impulses to overeat will more than likely end in excessive food consumption. Expect your previous symptoms and fat to rapidly return.
- People around you will be eating foods that you can't eat, and their food is going to look and smell better than yours'.
- If you expect to lose more weight than your body can handle, you will feel discouraged when you don't lose what you expect, and you'll feel punished and deprived by the food restrictions. Expect to cheat and lose less than your body can handle.
- You are still expected to follow the protocol when you're less motivated, when you aren't prepared, when you don't

have the right food with you, or when your food seems bland, dry, and tasteless.

- You might have headaches, low blood pressure, and many people feel cold most of the time.
- Some people experience hair loss during and/or after the protocol.
- Some people get skin rashes while injecting hCG.
- If you've been through menopause, you might randomly get your period.
- If you haven't been through menopause yet, your periods might be heavier.
- If you are still menstruating and are not on birth control, you're more likely to get pregnant while injecting hCG.
- It is common for people to have increased sex drive during the entire protocol.
- Certain gut imbalances might correct themselves.
- Autoimmune symptoms might get worse during the very low-calorie protocol, even though you've eliminated almost all food and are losing body fat. The symptoms usually correct themselves once the hCG is eliminated, food is increased, and your weight stabilizes.
- Your sleep might change from insomnia to deep and heavy sleep, and then back to insomnia, or visa versa.
- You are expected to follow the very low-calorie protocol for three to six weeks, no matter what life stress or celebration you experience. When that's done, your food restrictions are still modified for another three weeks.
- If you obsess over your weight loss during the protocol, you are more likely to stay obsessed about your weight after the protocol is over.
- If you take pride and display/show off your weight loss, you are more likely to have deep levels of embarrassment and shame if you gain it back.

- If you struggle with emotional eating and body-image issues, you're more at risk to make things worse if the protocol is approached like a diet.
- If you've struggled with an eating disorder in the past, expect it to resurface with a vengeance. Your bingeing will be worse, and purging might come back.

If done as a medical treatment rather than a body image-focused diet, you might feel better, you might sleep better, and other symptoms might also be alleviated too. Metabolic and hormonal imbalances might be corrected.

Here are two important questions:
1. If told the truth about the difficulty following the protocol, and what's realistic in terms of weight lost, how many people would hesitate before committing to an hCG diet?
2. Is the physical healing worth the sacrifice in limiting food for months, especially if there is no guarantee of the results, or that the results would last?

People need to understand the sacrifice, and realistically address the mindset it takes to restrict to the 500-calorie protocol without feeling punished, and entitled to a reward.

If hCG-diet businesses were honest about the process, people would see that the hCG protocol might not be realistic for them yet, or never. The food restrictions might not be good for their current life situation, or they might be too emotional about their weight, they might be traveling too much and can't keep a stable environment, or they will want to eat off protocol for certain life events.

Distorting the protocol to be easier than it actually is, and distorting the weight-loss expectations to be better than they really are, does a huge disservice to people who are

seeking information and help. It sets people up to be in the worst possible position in terms of being emotionally prepared for the limitations of doing the hCG protocol.

Being honest about what's expected in order to do the protocol correctly, what it's going to take to adhere to the protocol in real-life circumstances and change, and by being realistic about what to expect physically, a person can better understand if she is a good candidate for the process. Too many people jump into the protocol thinking the gratification of fat loss is all he or she needs in order to stay motivated. Unfortunately, this is the farthest thing from the truth.

Just because a person might physically and emotionally benefit hugely by losing excess body fat doesn't mean her issues with emotional eating will disappear. In reality, the more a person emotionalizes her body fat in a negative way, and the more shame she has about her body, the more likely she is to experience emotional eating and binge-eating patterns while on and also after the protocol.

Emotional Motivations to Lose Weight

The reasons people want to lose weight, and the emotional pressure they bring to the protocol, can distort everything. Even if they are mentally prepared for what is realistic, they will still hope (and expect) for what they are fantasizing it will do for them.

Unfortunately, most people attempt the hCG protocol because they want to:
- Feel better about themselves,
- Feel better about how they present themselves publicly,
- Prove they have value to society,
- Lose weight to feel pride of their wedding pictures, or
- To feel attractive enough to get out on the dating scene.

**The context for why you want to do the hCG protocol
has the power to make or break the long-term outcome
of the protocol, and ultimately should be evaluated by
each medical provider prior to prescribing hCG.**

The goal is to focus the protocol as a physical healing process and as medical treatment meant for the body and its intricate endocrine system. Similar to how other medical procedures are meant to impact the body, Dr. Simeons' hCG protocol should be approached the same way.

It is not meant as a solution for self-esteem issues, social insecurity, fear of judgment, or other personal issues stemming from emotional conflict. *If the participant can approach the protocol as a medical treatment to potentially heal the body, rather than a desire to be thinner and more accepted by society, then yes, the protocol works, and it is worth it.*

But the more the participant is using the hCG protocol as a means to fix her negative self-esteem and the emotional tension with her body, the less likely she will 1) adhere to the protocol, 2) finish the protocol, 3) follow through the different phases that are essential for stabilization—and 4) the more likely she is to return to behaviors that are direct causes for the physical consequence she wants to remove.

**Being that the hCG protocol was intended as
both a hormonal therapy and a medical process
specific to the metabolic physiology of the brain
and body, it would be incredibly risky to prescribe
and promote the protocol for people who have
significant emotional and psychological issues with
food as a coping mechanisms, and with their
body image—even if they are morbidly obese.**

High Expectations and the Pressure of Perfectionism

The problem is that the intensity of a participant's high expectations and emotional needs for weight loss is projected onto the intensity of the protocol restrictions. It comes across in the mind as tension or "stress." This increases the pressure for her to be perfect, which promotes an unforgiving all-or-nothing approach. If there is one deviation or misstep, even if it's minor, her mind equates it to complete failure, which increases her risk of bingeing while on the protocol. Or she might just quit mid-way, thinking that without perfection and the most amount of fat loss possible, finishing the protocol isn't worth it—despite the physical progress already made.

Because the effectiveness of the hCG protocol depends on being removed from the ease and liberal comfort of food, it's important the participant has an open mind about the entire process.

Not only must a person have a grasp of the sacrifices needed for her to stay on the protocol, but she needs to have a realistic grasp for what to expect in return.

If not, she is more likely to hold her body to fantasy expectations that aren't within reach; she will assume the protocol will be easier than it really is; and she will struggle when reality sets in. She will think the protocol doesn't work, feel burdened by the process, eat off the protocol, *or simply not finish the protocol.*

It's better to prepare for the opposite of what the diet culture promotes—and expect a difficult environment with the minimal results. If the participant can wrap his or her mind around that concept with an open mind about the healing process, she will be mentally prepared for difficulty, have an easier time adhering to the protocol (without feeling like a victim or martyr), and she will be more gracious and accepting if the body responds slowly.

This would require that the participant must let go of hope to achieve the imagery sold to her in false advertising. She also has to let go of the desire to be thinner even when that means she must surrender the emotional benefits. And ahead of time before losing weight, she'd have to address and resolve the emotional strain she has with her body and with food.

Every single person who reaches out for my help has some expectation she believes fat loss will give her, and she has an intensity and need for that result. There's an image or a fantasy in her mind about what being thinner will do for her. Whether it's a life without knee pain, freedom to eat emotionally again, a concept of health she's been sold, a more self-confident experience at the beach, a perfectly fitting wedding dress, proof that she still has her youth when she turns forty-five, earned pride from her mother when she sees her slimmer, superiority for quickly losing post-baby body fat, having done something better than her sister, or keeping her spouse from cheating again.

There's always an expectation people have attached to their desire to lose weight, and there's also an intensity that comes with it. How desperate are you to lose the weight?

SECTION 3

Body Image and Wanting to Lose Weight

Request for Robin's help:

"Hi Robin, I was midway through the hCG protocol when I came across your YouTube videos. I stopped weighing and was feeling great until now, one week into phase 3. I've been bingeing/purging for two days now.

"My dieting and orthorexia started five years ago, at the age of 40. I've binged and had body image issues all my adult life, but it wasn't until I found a serious weight-loss method (the hCG protocol, and intermittent fasting) that things started to spiral downhill and affect my life this much. I have two daughters, and I've also influenced them and want to stop that now.

I'm menopausal and wanted to do another hCG protocol round because I thought if my hormones are in balance, and I'm carrying less weight, the menopausal symptoms would ease…like dark moods, depression, lethargy, body odor, body temperature, etc.

"I've also spent the last year adjusting to major life changes: moved from Australia to Denmark, a new job, part-time work to full-time work, my husband became the stay-at-home parent, finding new friends....lots of changes, good and bad, and lots of weight gain. Can you help me?"

Chapter 6

The Twisted Relationship Between Dieting and Emotional Eating

"Our dependency makes slaves out of us, especially if this dependency is a dependency of our self-esteem. If you need encouragement, praise, pats on the back from everybody; then you make everybody your judge."
– Fritz Perls, founder of Gestalt therapy

Similar to a string of lights knotted into a mess that seems impossible to unravel, most people who come to me for help are trying to untangle the tight grip *between their relationship with food—and their relationship with their body.* They've entangled themselves in a co-dependent relationship with suffocating diets to fix the dysfunctional relationship they have with food and the shame they have with their body. No matter how hard they've tried to loosen and relax the problems, they end up with more confusion, more tension, and more difficulty separating the grip between wanting to be thinner and wanting to eat.

When people come to me, they understand two things:
1. They have difficulty managing their desire for food.
2. Their food issues conflict with their desire for being and staying thinner.

Some people have been told they might be addicted to food, others identify with an eating disorder, such as binge eating disorder. Some people come to me for help with emotional eating, thinking they need to learn self-restraint and increase their willpower. Whatever the reason, they believe their relationship with food is the main problem, and they are seeking help to get control.

For many of my clients, much of their waking day is held hostage by the suffocating pressure to eat right, managing every morsel of food that passes their lips, and trying to repress incessant desires to eat. Food has the power to make or break their day, and the more they struggle with food, the more pressure they have to restrict perfectly. With help, they are hoping for mercy.

People Seeking Help ...

- Don't understand why their desire for food is so high, despite the fact that they are desperate to be thinner and healthier.
- Can't stop thinking about food, what they can and cannot eat, and what they want to eat but shouldn't.
- Describe their fear of hunger, worry if they are going to get to eat, and constantly anticipate the next meal.
- Are burdened by anxiety about their body, what it looks like, what it weighs, how their clothes do or don't fit, their health, and what needs to be fixed.

Their hope is that I might somehow give them clarity on how to stop obsessing about food to minimize their emotional eating so they can peacefully do the hCG protocol to lose weight in order to feel better about themselves.

This is the type of approach they've come to expect as the businesses and people they've gone to for guidance in the past, have always reinforced food fears and restrictions with weight loss as motivation. It's easy to not recognize *that those dieting and weight loss pressures* are significant contributing factors to the overeating problem.

For most dieters, because having shame and fear of being overweight is constantly there, the pressure to restrict food is a constant too. In addition, the pressure to restrict intensifies the more weight a person thinks she might gain, or needs to lose, and the more shame she has about that weight. From this position it seems as if she'll never enjoy the pleasures of good food again, which promotes pre-diet overeating and post-diet overeating. This is like feasting before and after famine, especially when the pressure to restrict seems to be permanent.

To help clients get a sense of what it would be like removed from the incessant drive to eat, I discuss the option of permanently giving up all diets and judgments about food. I ask:

What would it feel like if you never had to diet for the rest of your life?

Almost all of the people I pose this question to feel immediate relief—but without food restrictions they realize they'll never lose weight again, and that terrifies them. Accepting the vulnerability of their body fat without having control over it seems impossible.

To these clients, giving up food restrictions and dieting seems as if they'd have to:
- Allow body fat to stay on their body.
- Accept they'll never be thinner.
- Accept that without controls to guide eating, they'd have to live with the consequences of weight gain if they "lose control."

- Based on their negative perspectives about body fat, to accept inferiority, inadequacy, judgment, rejection, embarrassment, isolation, and being alone.

With this way of thinking, accepting you'll never diet again means you'll never be thinner, which can feel like accepting a life of emotional and physical misery. This makes dieting seem virtuous, despite the agitation to overeat and the stress about eating that food restrictions often trigger. Controlling food intake would seem like the right thing to do, especially when weight is gained because of overeating behavior. However, much of that behavior is negotiated, assuming the gained weight would get removed with a future diet. Unfortunately, this means the pressure to restrict food and resulting overeating, seems like a never-ending cycle that's impossible to resolve because the dogma about being thinner apparently isn't negotiable.

This is like being backed into a corner where there's pain and suffering no matter what direction you turn. You're either miserable as food and dieting has hijacked your life, or you're emotionally pained by having to remain in a perceived undesirable heavier body. The only option available to relieve the misery of perpetual dieting and overeating that has taken over your entire purpose in life is this: to let go of being thinner and to accept the perceived negative conditions of the body that food restrictions apparently fix.

To do this it would take understanding:
- Why being thinner doesn't seem to be negotiable, despite huge variability in race and genetics.
- Why being thinner is so important to you.
- What you stand to lose giving it up.
- What you gain in freedom when food restrictions and shame for eating disappear.
- How dieting has enabled excessive emotional eating.
- That you must take emotional responsibility for feelings

of insecurity in life without turning to eating food to cope.

You have to question the beliefs you have about being thinner and rethink the relationship you have with dieting, emotional eating, your body, and what you want to do with the life that body gives you.

In order to address the emotional strain and pressure between dieting and overeating, I believe it is vitally important that the underlying reasons for why body fat comes with such negative stigma must be questioned and discussed.

The issue must be looked at from a distance to see why the way the body is perceived as so defining to culture, and how that feedback is used to define a person's internal sense of worth. The relationship people have with their body must be looked at, especially in a culture that promotes the glorification of thinness. If conformed to, we must address how worshipping thinness as a symbol of superior quality impacts how people emotionally relate to dieting and weight-loss programs, especially how that influences survival mechanisms wired to secure access to food in defense of life.

How Intense is Your Desire to Lose Weight?

Almost every time the hCG protocol clinic received an enquiring call, email, or walk-in, the person who was interested and seeking information about the program had a strong need to lose weight. It was like he or she had no choice in the matter. Most people had years, and often decades, of focus, dedication, study, and effort trying to fix their size and/or weight. This was the story each person brought to the clinic, no matter how thin or large they were. They all felt a similar unhappiness with their body which is what brought them to seek something as restrictive as the 500 very low-calorie protocol.

Ask yourself:

**How unsettled and insecure a person must be with her
body to do something as radically restrictive as Dr. Simeons'
500-calorie hCG protocol—for emotional reasons?
The answer: very.**

However, not everyone's unhappiness with their body had the same intensity. Not every person who weighed over 250 pounds felt equally as bad about it. Not all people who were 20 pounds heavier than they were a year prior felt the same level of shame and embarrassment from not fitting into their thinner clothes. Not all of our clients monitored their weight multiple times a day or had the same frantic desperation to strictly control their food.

As we saw variation in people's weight and size, we saw variable intensity in how people felt about their body. Similar to how volume goes up and down, the "volume" of a person's negativity about her body can go up and down, and it doesn't necessarily match the size of her body.

Some people who are thinner feel equally as upset about their weight as a person who is morbidly obese, and the largest clients don't necessarily have the largest dissatisfaction with their body, or the strongest desire to lose weight.

**How people evaluate their body isn't necessarily in line
with reality or the truthful state of their body.**

The intensity of a person's motivation to lose weight can be explained by how important that goal is to her emotionally.

- How essential is it for happiness, and how much fat loss is definably necessary?
- How much does the desire to lose weight come from a desire to enable emotional eating?

- How thin does he or she need to be, and how much pressure is there to keep the weight off?
- How quickly do they need weight loss to happen?

All of these factors impact the intensity behind the drive to diet.

When it comes to the restrictions of the hCG protocol, it's very attractive to people who have more intense feelings about their body fat and needs to lose weight quickly. In these cases, the hCG protocol is attractive in three ways:

1.) The amount of fat lost is typically significant for larger people.
2.) The amount of time away from food is shorter. The protocol fits not only their need to lose a large sum of body fat, but also their need to be away from food for the shortest time possible.
3.) For others, the protocol is appealing because of its radically restrictive food controls. This is attractive for people who are already accustomed to extreme dieting or chronically restricting food.

Despite the obvious extreme nature of the protocol, difficulty preparing for it and actually doing it, the protocol is very attractive to those who have the most emotional problems with food, their body, and the most intense emotional desire to be thinner. Even if you aren't a chronic dieter, the idea that you could actually reach the thinness you once used to be (or that you've never yet achieved) can create an intense emotional response.

> **NOTE:** The discontent a person has with her body isn't measured only by the difference between what she has and what she wants, but it's also magnified by the importance of what she wants. For example, a woman who is getting married might hold herself more strictly to the ideals of a thinner body, especially ideals promoted

by those in wedding magazines. The magnified importance of being thinner at her wedding, and for wedding pictures, increases the criticism and unhappiness with her body, even when she was content at the same size before getting engaged. The way she normally felt about her body was more lenient and relaxed before the importance perfectionism of her wedding came into mind. This is a great example of how some people increase or decrease their need for meeting physical expectations—depending on the importance of the environment to which they are exposed.

Another example of this is how a person might feel about her body before and after committing to a vacation where she will be wearing a bathing suit in public. Before knowing she was going on a vacation, she might have been easy going about her desire to be thinner. After committing to the vacation, she might feel worse about her body, building pressure and tension to lose weight.

Her body is blamed as the source of stress, especially when there's a time frame set to reach a certain goal.

Rate Your Dissatisfaction

One of the ways I try to grasp the intensity behind a person's feelings and need to lose weight is based *how she reacts to the idea that she will never lose weight again.* I have the client describe how she'd feel if her body had to stay the same for the rest of her life, as if it was permanently impossible for her to lose weight or be thinner. I observe the descriptions of how she feels about it, and then I have her rate the detriment to her life not being able to lose weight is, using a scale from one to ten (ten being catastrophic hardship and one being the least troubling).

As people experience the emotions connected to having to stay the same, stigma and negative beliefs about bodyfat increase and predictably they catastrophically rate their body. What I've found fascinating is that as soon as a person is forced to exist in her unfixed body, without any possibility of change, she'd first rate the negative impact, dissatisfaction, and life hardship between a nine or a ten.

> **It didn't matter if she was 10 pounds or a 100 pounds overweight—when the body at its current state was made permanent, her level of dissatisfaction immediately intensified.**

It was as if permanent connection to her existing body would forever and permanently make her feel lacking, unattractive, inferior, unworthy, a failure, unhappy, and disconnected from an enjoyable life. But when I have clients rate the hardship of other more-difficult physical limitation, their feelings began to change.

Once she's rated the hardship of *never being thinner,* then I have clients visualize having to experience increased damages to their body, and I progressively make those damages more limiting. I ask how they'd react and rate permanent physical loss like losing the use of their legs after a car accident, compared to losing the use of their arms. I have them visualize how they'd feel about and rate the hardship of permanently losing their eyesight, hearing, or even having to live with permanent disfigurement, like having burn scars all over their head and face. With each permanent physical loss, *they'd rethink what a nine or a ten was in terms of hardship.*

Eventually I ask again how she'd rate the dissatisfaction and hardship of life if her body had to remain exactly how it was with its current amount of body fat, never being thinner. To most people's surprise, they could see the relativity and the prior distortion in the grievance and dissatisfaction with their body.

> **The body fat she previously catastrophized and thought made life a horrific adversity now seems petty, and**

what she rated a nine or a ten in life hardship
before moves down the scale to a zero, one, or a two.

For many people, it is very relieving to recognize when their negative perceptions are distorted because being aware of this gives them a sense of freedom and lenience with their body without having to aggressively fix it. People realize they don't actually have a body that can't be accepted, adapted to, or appreciated.

Observing people's immediate shift in perceptions about their body brought me to ponder how beliefs about being thinner as a symbol of being superior plays a role in encouraging a twisted emotional relationship towards one's own body. As well, how those ideals about being thinner project into and distort people's relationship with dieting and emotional eating. What I observed over and over again was that as ideal body images held in their mind lost power, people felt a release in the pressure to diet as well as a relaxation in the urges to eat emotionally.

As the pressure to lose weight went away,
so did tensions to restrict food
and impulses to overeat.

Distorted Perceptions About Your Body and Food

Having people visualize themselves in a body with worse permanent restrictions, and more limiting ability, helps them see how negative feelings about their body can cognitively distort their perceptions about food.

> **NOTE:** Cognitive distortions are biased beliefs or subjective viewpoints about oneself, and ultimately about the world around them. If we look at what distortion means, understanding how people with completely different body shapes and size feel the exact same negativity makes more sense. According to the *Merriam-Webster*

Dictionary the definition of distortion is the act of twisting or altering something out of its true, natural, or original state.

I believe distorted views and beliefs often stem from fears of danger that trigger self-defense mechanisms that alter perceptions based on what a person needs to survive.

> **People's viewpoints become biased toward perceptions of self-preservation, and focused toward getting what they need to feel safe and protected from what they think is threatening.**

Their view is focused on magnifying what is perceived as dangerous, and is fixated on magnifying what is perceived as safe. Their view doesn't necessarily match reality, or what is rational or objective. As if a state of survival shifts the mind to predict, defend, and protect oneself from threat—shifting the mind to perceive everything from a viewpoint of "danger."

Dr. David D. Burns researched the topic, and in his book, The Feeling Good Handbook (1989), he describes these thought patterns. Some of the examples of cognitive distortions described by Burns are:

- **All-or-nothing thinking:** You look at things in absolute, black-and-white categories.
- **Over-generalization:** You view a negative event as a never-ending pattern of defeat.
- **Mental filter:** You dwell on the negative.
- **Discounting the positives:** You insist that your accomplishments or positive qualities don't count.
- **Jumping to conclusions:**
  A) Mind-reading: you assume that people are reacting negatively to you when there's no definite evidence.
  B) Fortune Telling: you arbitrarily predict that things will turn out badly.

- **Magnification or minimization:** You blow things way out of proportion or you shrink their importance.
- **Emotional reasoning:** You reason from how you feel: "I feel like an idiot, so I really must be one."
- **"Should statements":** You criticize yourself (or other people) with "shoulds," "oughts," "musts," and "have tos."
- **Labeling:** Instead of saying "I made a mistake," you tell yourself, "I'm a jerk, or "a fool," or a "loser."
- **Personalization and blame:** You blame yourself for something you weren't entirely responsible for, or you blame other people and deny your role in the problem.

I've observed that many people attracted to more extreme diet restrictions, like Dr. Simeons' hCG protocol, have emotional needs to lose weight that seem to stem from many of these cognitive distortions. Especially true is the magnifying or catastrophizing of their weight, the danger of food, and the difficulty of food restrictions. This is why visualizing different complications and potential limitations with the body is so helpful, as relieving "dangers" about one's body fat ultimately undistorts how people relate to food.

In order to unravel the stress and impulses people experience with dieting and emotional eating, they must first untwist the distortions they have with their body.

To do this, they will need to question the beliefs that bring them to be negative or unhappy with their body in the first place.

Is Weight Loss a Need or a Want?

At the medical hCG protocol clinic I worked at, no matter how much weight clients wanted to lose, they came to us with a similar desperation for help, and willingness to commit if we could convince them our program would work to help them lose weight. Each person who came to our clinic had a passionate distaste for whatever amount of fat they had. Their reason for losing weight was filled with good intentions, and they believed the hCG protocol would be their miracle cure.

It didn't matter if they clearly weren't good candidates for the very low-calorie protocol because they were too lean. If they believed they had a weight problem, even if it was a perceived five to ten pounds too much, because they felt their extra body fat was "bad," they assumed we would agree and were obligated to help them lose weight.

> **People assumed that no matter what, their desires
> to lose weight were factual needs, as if being
> thinner wasn't negotiable.**

We made it a point to question the intentions and motivations of each person who wanted to lose weight with our program. We asked each person 1) why they felt bad about their body, 2) why wasn't their body good enough, 3) what fears they attached to their body, and 4) what did they expect weight loss would do for them. Not one person inquiring about our service expected their desire to lose weight *to be questioned.* I assume this could be due to years of diet programs agreeing with their desperate need to be thinner, but when we didn't agree with their rationale or that they had excess fat to lose, people were often shocked and sometimes angry. *They believed that we, too, should agree that no matter what, they needed to lose weight.*

When these people's desire to lose weight has always been agreed upon by the businesses/weight loss industry capitalizing on the concept of "thinner is better," it's shocking for their desire to lose weight to be questioned.

> **It's not that we didn't empathize with the negative
> emotions and desperation people brought into the clinic,
> but we knew many of these people believed they needed
> to be thinner, when in fact *they were perfectly healthy.***

I speculate only 5–10 percent of the people who came to the clinic who wanted to do the hCG protocol actually met Dr. Simeons' criteria as "diseased."

Even if they had adequate body fat, making them good candidates physically for the very-low calorie protocol, if their need and emphasis to lose weight wasn't to help the body but was based on these following reasons, we discouraged the hCG protocol. Reasons were: 1. Desire to improve negative feelings about their body, 2. To control over eating, 3. To fix a struggling relationship with a loved one, 4. To impress a parent, or 5. To compensate for a loss or failure in another area of life. In those cases, they first need professional help from a therapist—not a weight-loss program.

> **EXAMPLE:** A 40-year old woman came into the clinic desperate for help. Perfectly dressed in her business attire, heels, and with perfectly manicured makeup and hair, she pointed to her hipbone. She acknowledged it didn't seem like a problem to anybody else, but that to her it was a REAL problem. Her clothes felt tight and she wanted to get rid of the pocket of fat on her hip because it was a terrible for her health. "I know for other people this isn't a problem, but I know my body and I usually don't have this problem. Plus, my knees have been hurting and I think by losing five to ten pounds my hormones won't be so out of sorts, and my knees will feel better."
>
> She confidently explained how healthy her diet was and how her weight was easily maintained with her sugar-free, grain-free, nut-free, dairy-free, preservative-free, GMO-free, super-controlled diet. However, because her knees started hurting during her high intensity weight-training classes, she couldn't exercise, and since then has felt out of control, allowing herself to drink more wine and have some sugar. This client described how she had gained 7.38 pounds, convinced the sugar was causing her weight gain and making her knee pain worse. "I can tell this added weight is mak-

ing it harder on my knees. It's just not healthy, and I can tell the sugar is making my hormones go crazy." She was hoping the protocol would help her get under her 112-pound goal and get her sugar cravings under control.

When we questioned her dieting history, she opened up about her childhood weight problem. She talked about how she perceived her parents to be very unhealthy, and how she was embarrassed to have friends over. When she left home for college, she decided to better herself and to lose weight. Since then she's been able to maintain her thinness with strict focus, dedication, and control. She was convinced she was addicted to sugar and believed her food restrictions were the best thing for her health and weight.

She discovered the hCG protocol after someone in an on-line diet forum mentioned she might have hormone issues that the protocol could fix. She was convinced she had hormonal problems caused by the sugar, and she believed she was a good candidate for the hCG protocol. Recognizing her clear and obvious distorted perceptions, we turned her away.

Someone like this 40-year-old woman wouldn't be attracted to just any type of restriction. Her needs were so intense that she actually counted her weight gain by the .38 of a pound measurement. Any time a client described their losses and gains by the .01 value, it is a clear indication of how important their weight is, and how valuable the weight adjustments are, in gain and loss.

Considering her normal way of eating requires such extreme restriction already, it wouldn't make sense that she'd be attracted to a moderate approach to dieting. The 500 calories on the hCG protocol was a good fit for both her already-existing restriction, and her desperate need to lose the extra 7 (and .38) extra pounds. Her needs for thinness were extreme, and so were her feelings about being fat. It is that type of intensity that attracts people to the hCG protocol, despite its extreme demands.

It doesn't matter if a person is 450 pounds or 115 pounds, if you believe you need to lose weight, some other people as well as the weight-loss businesses will support your logic without question.

The lean 40-year old woman in the example believed the fat loss would make her feel safe again, that losing the extra 7.38 pounds would give her the motivation to go back to her radical restrictions, that it would actually relieve the pain in her knees, and that it would return her "thinner and healthier" security. Her beliefs clearly came from distortions that catastrophized her body.

For others, the reason they want to lose weight is to remove physical limitations and risks associated with their larger size, in order to feel they are safe to go back to eating in order to cope with emotional stresses in life. Each pound of fat lost gets them closer to being able to reward themselves with eating again, and in these cases, the restrictions are typically magnified to be harder to follow than the truthfully are.

Whatever the need, most people never think to question their desire to lose weight and what brings them to believe radical restrictions, like the 500-calorie hCG protocol, will make everything better.

To understand your urge and gravitation toward dieting, you'd have to question the negative feelings you have about your body and what losing weight will do for you emotionally.

Chapter 7

"Fitting In" with a Body Image

"There is nothing wrong with your body, but there is a lot wrong with the messages which try to convince you otherwise."
– Rae Smith, award-winning theatre designer

Where Negative Feelings About Body Fat Come From

When you consider how you feel about your body, your conclusions are probably based on images given to you by what is predictively promoted as superior by the people and culture in which you want to be identified and included. The positive ideal body pictured in your mind is a predictable conceptualized image repeated and promoted in a way that's associated with praise and inclusion. Naturally, when a person wants to be accepted, she seeks to become what is positively promoted by important people around her. To do this, she'd have to compare herself to the concept outside of what she's being encouraged to be, and from there work to conform.

This type of *Social Comparison* is commonly how people come to understand if they "fit in."

NOTE: In 1954, Leon Festinger, a social psychologist, proposed that when a person can't find a fair or objective understanding of if she's "acceptable," she often compares herself to others in order to fulfill the basic human drive for that type of self-evaluation.[1]

The more often people see repeated glamourized and promoted images of the body, the more likely they are to compare themselves to those images to assess their acceptability.[1] The goal is to not stand out as different, especially if different equates to being seen as bad or inferior. Not fitting in would feel as if you're an outcast, aren't worthy, and aren't welcome.

When what the media portrays, and the people who are praised, are all thin and look similar, evaluating oneself in contrast to those images to see how you compare would be understandable. As a result, it would be expected for most "normal" or larger people to feel bad about their size and weight, especially women who compare themselves to consistent images in the media that are considered on average to be 20 percent underweight.[2]

Today, more often than not, the images that are promoted are air brushed and unnaturally distorted. Arms are thinned out, necks and legs are extended, butts, boobs, and lips are magnified, hair is made to look thicker, etc. For this reason, I assume almost 100 percent of people who repeatedly see *and believe that these images are attainable* will assume their body, in comparison, is inadequate.

Add to that how often girls and boys are bombarded with unrealistic glamourized images promoted by businesses like the weight-loss industry, and people idolized in social media, making a financial profit selling products, programs, and services that apparently help consumers "fit in."

Most people don't recognize that the opinions they have about theirs and another's body usually stem from unrealistic physical images and ideals that are promoted consistently by family, friends, and what's in the media. When a person's body is judged negatively, it probably stems from being compared to these repeated images.

> **Although, it might seem as if the negativity is coming from the "bad" body, it's actually coming from ideals being enforced on everyone as unquestionable truth.**

Without awareness or question, those ideals are given credibility, which means the person being judged is perceived as convincingly and truthfully flawed.

And as "health" is commonly paired with a thin body image, goals that are promoted as healthy are actually disguised vanity-based pursuits, and a "healthy" lifestyle is often undertaken for the sake of "fitting in" by being viewed as attractive, *not necessarily for health.*[3]

Unfortunately, associating health with how thin a person is has taught that body fat is a visible mark of illness, disease, and unhealth. This assumption has resulted in stigma of weight and body fat, as if being larger is an indication or symbol of "badness" and inferiority, similar to how in times past thinness was stigmatized when it was associated with being poor, poverty, disease, and death.

Stigma

The term *stigma* dates back to the Greeks. They cut or burned marks into the skin of criminals, slaves, and traitors in order to visibly identify them as tainted or immoral people who should be avoided.[4] Today, it is not a physical mark but instead an attribute that results in widespread social disapproval.

> **NOTE:** Stigma has three fundamental components: 1) recognizing difference, 2) devaluation because of that difference, and 3) that it occurs in social interactions. Because of this, stigma does not reside

in the person but rather in the social context, therefore, what is stigmatizing in one social context may not be stigmatizing in another situation.[4]

As it relates to obesity, weight bias and stigma assumes, when compared to the superior thinner ideal, the more fat a person has *is a mark of disgrace, which defines his or her character and quality as a person as inferior.*

Excess weight is the fourth prevalent source of discrimination, behind gender, race, and age, and unfortunately, stigmatization and bullying can start very early in a child's life.[5]

The idea is that obesity is a choice—that people who are obese choose to lack self-discipline, are lazy, and are inferior human beings. This ignorant attitude is deeply ingrained in public psyche, and the judgment towards obesity has affected millions of people, causing serious psychological consequences, and adverse effects to their physical health.

Weight Stigma at Work and within the Medical Community

- In a study of 2,449 obese and overweight women, 72 percent experienced a source of bias against them because of their weight.[6]
- According to the National Education Association, more people experience bullying in the workplace for their weight than for sexual orientation, disability, sexual harassment, race, or religion. (2011)
- To make matters worse, 69 percent of the women experienced bias from medical professionals.[6]
- Also, levels of implied weight bias among dietitians are higher than the general population at 52 percent.[8]
- Among dietitians and dietetic students, most expressed

anger and frustration with patients, assumed patients lack commitment, motivation, and compliance with health behavior changes.[7]

- Of dietitians polled, 76 percent expressed moderate-to-high levels of unspoken weight bias.[7, 8]

- A 2012 study disclosed that attitudes of medical professionals toward obese patients showed that they viewed these patients as lazy, lacking self-control, weak, sloppy, unsuccessful, dishonest, and non-compliant.[7, 9]

- As a patient's Body Mass Index (BMI) increases, physicians report having less patience, less desire to help, felt that seeing obese patients is a waste of their time, and having less respect for patients.[10, 9]

- It is not uncommon for obesity to be the topic of jokes in medical schools. Of 4,732 first-year medical students from 49 different medical schools, the majority of students expressed open and private feelings of very strong anti-fat weight bias.[11]

- When patients visit medical providers, they can sense discrimination and stigma. Parents of obese children often express feelings of being blamed by doctors, and so do adult patients. They feel berated, disrespected, and upset by many of the derogatory comments made about their weight.[12]

- **Providers spent less time in appointments with obese patients and had less discussion with less intervention.[12, 11] As a result, patients are less likely to get preventive services, exams, cancer screens, pelvic exams, mammograms, and are more likely to delay, prevent, or cancel appointments and services.[13, 11]**

- In a study of over 1,060 adults, when asked: if your doctor would refer to your weight in a stigmatized negative way— almost half of the people said they'd feel upset, embarrassed, and would feel bad about themselves.[12] As a consequence, patients are more likely to avoid future health care, which in the end, increases the likelihood that medical problems won't getting attended to.[11]

It doesn't help that dieticians, physicians, and the medical community in general, is misinformed by 1) their own bias, 2) outdated concepts stemming from the 1940's height-and-weight chart, and 3) ignorant assumptions that obesity is a matter of "not wanting it enough" or laziness.

Those considered the "authority," are unintentionally unaware of the impact their naive ignorance has on the entire diet, health, and weight-loss industry, as well as the attitudes of society as a whole, only because they are regarded as credible sources of "health" information.

Because of stigma coming from these "health" belief systems, the desire someone has to be and stay thinner isn't questioned nor is it looked at as a subjective opinion. In general, dieters (no matter what size) have similar fear of food, shame of body fat, desires to be thinner, and beliefs about what weight loss will provide for them. All of which makes the desire to be thinner feel objective. This is like being brainwashed, making food restriction an unquestionable virtue, to the point where people often think dieting is as important and defining as religious doctrine. From an observer's point of view, this makes the body image they are seeking foreseeable, and the food they praise and demonize predictable.

Internalization, Brain Washing, and "Your" Opinion

When I suffered with an eating disorder, I thought I was holding myself to a physical concept that was my own. But the truth is the image I was seeking was the image promoted in fitness magazines, and was also the lean and muscular body associated with professional athletes.

92

At some point I innocently accepted the socially praised image—and believed the positive feelings I had about it were coming from my own desires.
This is the premise of internalization.

Internalization is when an individual accepts group, social, or cultural standards, beliefs, and images as the sacred, unquestionable truth, and then incorporates those ideals in her mind as her own. This makes it seem as if those opinions are part of her personal self-concept. She identifies culturally accepted subjective concepts as objective personal truth within herself.

For example, when a person internalizes a culturally constructed image of the body that's encouraged in a positive way (like having a bigger butt, bigger lips, or thicker eyebrows), she will think it's her personal desire that her body should be that way. Predictably, she'll buy the products and services being sold that are pushing these images of the body, assuming she's compelled to do so because of her own personal viewpoint. She isn't consciously aware that her motivation to be accepted by "fitting in" is driving her feelings of positivity in complying to what these businesses are directing.

> **EXAMPLE:** Almost every client I've ever worked with has said: *"I don't care what other people think about my body anymore. I want to be thinner for me, so that I can feel better about myself."*

> She cannot see that her goal is predictably based on praised cultural dogma that she has internalized. In reality, it isn't "her goal" she's wanting to achieve to feel better about herself. Her goal is a concept that everyone is "supposed" to follow. She doesn't see that she feels bad about herself only because she's internalized that she too should conform to that praised image in order to feel worthy of inclusion.

> Remarks like, "My body doesn't look like 'Me'" or "I want my body back," shows that she claims ownership of a more ideal and posi-

tively promoted body image in her mind as her own. If her body doesn't match the culturally promoted and glamourized image held in her mind, unsurprisingly she will think her natural body is wrong. Her natural body isn't the one her culture wants or agrees with, and consequently, once internalized she doesn't agree with or want her natural body either.

When a person defines her worth by being able to conform to socially praised images of the body, and her body doesn't match, the result is to assume her body is taking worth away from her. Unfortunately, the aftereffect is feeling victimized by the body, as if the body is "bad." This is the basis for a "negative" body image, and it would seem as if fixing her body to match what is "good" and praised would help her feel positive about herself.

> **Basing one's worth on an internalized image of the body**
> *is the basic premise and definition of "body image."*
> **It is how a person comes to feel about herself, once her**
> **body is measured against the internalized ideal.**

Body Image

The traditional understanding of body image is that it is an internalized mental image of the body a person identifies by and wants, typically represented by what is seen positively by others. *The idea is that a positively seen body reflects a positive inner-self.* It's as though the body—its function, its looks, and other's opinion about it—symbolizes our value as a human, and can then be used to identify the quality and character of the person we are.

Thus, we are led to believe:

> **If your body is praised, it's because your body**
> **is superior…making you superior.**

**If your body is criticized, it's because your body
is inferior...making you inferior.**

For a person to praise or criticize her body, she must first have an internalized body-image model of correctness in her mind, to which she identifies by and then compares her body to. That comparison dictates how she feels about herself, and how she defines her relationship with her body in a positive or negative way. It's a matter of conforming the body to an acceptable image in order to prove the life it gives is safe, has value, and "fits in" to the world.

> **Stigma and People's Attraction to the HCG Protocol:** When body fat is stigmatized and morally shamed as a symbol of "badness," believers will do whatever is necessary to avoid being seen as an outcast. I assume how people feel about body fat today is similar to how it must have felt to have leprosy during biblical times. People were ashamed to go out in public for fear of being shunned or shamed for their body, as they desperately sought a cure.
>
> Wouldn't you sacrifice your freedom to eat to do the hCG protocol if it is your body fat cure? In effect, when approached like a diet, the protocol is used to cure people's stigma, shame, fear, and the visible symbol of their inadequacy. With these beliefs about body fat, people will do whatever it takes, no matter how hard it is, or how inappropriate it might be for their current physical or emotional state.

Are You a Thin Supremist?

No one questions why a person would feel ashamed and want to hide when she feels negatively about her body fat. It's assumed everyone wants to be thinner, especially when the diet and health industry continuously mongers fear with distorted perceptions that *at any cost, you should do whatever it takes to be thin, stay thin, and always to be leaner than you are.*

The goal set for you to "fit in" is for your body to be as fat free as possible, and the leaner you are, the more positively you are seen. Thinness is a symbol of health, worth, value, and superiority. I call this belief and goal system "thin supremacy." If you believe that leaner and thinner people are better, superior, and higher quality human beings—you are a thin supremist.

When you think about thin supremacy, think of it as a constructed concept that decides if you're acceptable or not based on how much weight you can lose or how thin you can be. In a thin-supremist culture, "negative" body image means you feel bad that you aren't thinner.

- When you hear someone say she wants to lose weight to feel better about herself, what you are hearing is a person who believes the condition of her body in relation to thin supremacy, *defines her sense of worth.*
- When she says she has a negative body image, she is saying she is inferior *because her body isn't thin enough to "fit in."*
- When you hear her say she feels better about herself when she loses weight, you are actually hearing that *she feels safe only if her body looks the way thin supremacists will praise, or won't judge.*
- When the way a person feels about her body is bad, it makes sense she would believe the only way to feel better about it would be to *conform her body to the image in her mind that she's judging herself by.* If that image is based on thin supremacy, she must diet, restrict food, and do whatever it takes to get her body to comply.

However, when body image is seen as a concept rather than a truth, there is an alternative way to be free from feeling bad. It would be to accept the truth of your body as it naturally is, and to deny the idealized image and recognize it is unacceptably unrealistic and superficially vain. You'd have to define your worth separate from a body image, and to refuse internalizing thin supremacy, even when loved ones believe it.

Still, when not being thin enough is stigmatized as a sign of personal failure and inferiority, accepting the body unconditionally isn't that simple. When the people you care about, care about thinness, accepting your body when it isn't perceived as good enough, would be like accepting you don't fit in, and that your loved ones don't think you're good enough either.

Chapter 8

When Your Body Is Your Biggest Threat

"In order to have freedom from feelings of emotional deprivation, it's very important with any weight loss that the individual separate his/her definition of personal value from his/her body, from needing restriction for control or from excessiveness. This prevents an ego dependent on physical accomplishment from experiencing shame associated with fat gain, and allows the individual to rationally take care of his/her body without expecting, or being entitled to, an emotional reward in return."
– *Weight-Loss Apocalypse-1*, chapter 2 page 39

"Fitting In" with Family

People come to internalize ideal body images in their mind for many different reasons: family beliefs, religious ideals, perceptions of what health or illness is, athletic ability, perceived sexuality, culture, race, the media, etc.

In cultures that commonly accept thin supremacy, people assume, without question, the need to be thin is real and true. If you are a larger person trying to fit into these cultures, it would be expected for you to pursue fat-reducing weight-loss programs. And if you don't, you are seen as flawed, dumb, lazy, inadequate, inferior, and worthy of being excluded. When you're raised in an environment where being thinner is worshiped and being fatter is punished, it would make sense that you'd pursue what is seen positively by those you love.

Children do not question their family's attitudes toward body image, so when experiencing praise or criticism, it would seem natural to attach the attitude to the body.

What is perceived positively about the body by those we care about develops into a mental image of what we personally want from the body in order to 1) feel secure with ourselves, 2) safe with others, and 3) socially accepted.

When important people in your life fixate on the conditions of their own body and the body of others, wanting their approval and fearing their disapproval regarding your own body would be understandable. Feeling wanted, included, and loved by the people you need and admire is at the core of who we are as humans, so it would be expected that we innocently want compliments, but we also fear criticism by those we love.

As some people are uplifted and praised for the conditions of the body, we see that others are put down and demeaned for having different physical conditions. *Therefore, if you don't have superior qualities, you are seen as inferior.* Whether the person is too short or too tall, is a different race, has lots of freckles, wears different religious clothing, has different hair, is too small or is too big—the body can be stigmatized as bad, flawed, or unhealthy by those who believe the "superior" type of body is the only acceptable body.

For a child, being judged by family or other important people for having an incorrect or "bad" body becomes a source of disapproval or being "in trouble." It can be a source of long-term pain and discontent with those relationships and your body.

The truth is, the loved ones that are critical of your weight probably fear that if your body doesn't conform to fit in, you'll be excluded. Even though it might seem they are criticizing you, they are actually criticizing and fearing that you will be rejected and disapproved of. This type of family criticism is a distorted form of love.

Growing Up Excluded

I've had countless clients who continued to suffer into adulthood, trying to recover from the way they were treated as young children because of their body. Some people were defined by the success of their physique, and as adults they continue with desperation to hold onto those positively seen aspects of their body. However, the majority of people I work with are trying to recover from the belief their body was, and still is, shameful and "bad"— and that they deserve to be excluded.

As kids, they…

- Were negatively compared to morbidly obese relatives, and were threatened that they were unhealthy and would die early.
- Felt punished when they were put on restrictive diets while siblings and friends were free to eat liberally and were safe from criticism.
- Were compared with thinner siblings, told they'd be more attractive if they'd lose weight, and their weight was a source of jokes, with people making fun of them.
- Experienced judgment from classmates and were shamed when they went to the doctor for checkups.
- Found that their size and weight became a significant hindrance to their excitement for physical activity and playing sports because of fear they wouldn't be accepted on a team.

For children who are perceived negatively because of their weight, this is like being punished as if they've done something wrong, or that something is wrong with whom they are. And socially they can be discarded and treated as if they are disobedient or "bad" people. The praised body image begins to define who she is and becomes her own measuring stick, defining if she's acceptable and lovable, or worthy of being rejected and abandoned.

> **For some, reaching socially defined body-image goals isn't about being praised or being seen as better than others so much as it's about avoiding criticism and having a sense of worth that others will approve of.**

Even if you don't care what other people think, if you are personally enforcing a superior image of the body, you are rejecting the ease and nature of your own body for what it inherently is, in exchange for some benefit that requires difficulty and work to make your body something it naturally isn't.

Consequently, your relationship with the body goes from accepting, loving, and free to being conditional, critical, self-centered, and controlling. Your body becomes your biggest enemy. It's no wonder people are emotionally attracted to the hCG protocol. It could be their miracle cure to remove stigma and to finally "fit in."

Survival Mode

When I talk with people who struggle with emotional eating, or eating disorders, they each have similar fears with similar terror-like intensity. But for most people, the fear doesn't start that intense, which is why anxiety is hard to identify. You wouldn't suspect something as innocent as wanting to be thinner as being "dangerous." *But when that desire is backed by primitive survival needs, nothing is innocent.*

Survival needs cognitively distort and magnify anything it latches onto, making seemingly simple and ordinary ideas into radicalized notions. And as those notions become less and less flexible and more and more rigid, survival mechanisms gradually distort notions into zealotry and dogma. In terms of idealizing thinness or thin supremacy, fatter conditions of the body become a perceived threat to life, and the mind then responds accordingly. When you "feel" fat you are actually feeling threat, as if you are easy prey to a predator. I recall this is what feeling "fat" felt like:

- It started with a dark, impending doom, and my body would involuntarily respond.
- I'd feel a flash of heat, my breathing felt compressed, and I'd start to sweat.
- My heart would beat so fast and hard it felt like it was going to come out of my chest.
- My hair would stand up on end.
- My stomach would hurt, and I'd feel nauseous, and it felt as if I was going to explode if something wasn't done immediately.
- My thoughts became erratic, like being short-circuited, and I couldn't think straight.
- It felt as if I was seeing through tunnel vision.
- My entire mind and body had an intense urgency to do something *now*.
- A horrible threat was there, and I needed to escape *right now*—as if there was extreme danger or emergency.

Each and every person I've worked with has described similar sensations. For some people, the feelings of impending doom or peril come when she feels deprived of food, and the only way to get rid of that horrible feeling is to eat. For others, threat is attached to gaining weight, which is why she micro-manages food and exercises obsessively. Like me, some people experience this impending doom with both food restriction and gaining weight, which is why they obsessively diet, and compulsively binge and then purge.

This has brought me to ponder the influence that both the fight-or-flight response and the controlling nature of sustained survival mode have on the construct of body image, the impulse to diet, and resultant emotional eating.

Survival mode is hard-wired physiological, psychological, and behavioral mechanisms triggered by apparent insecurity to handle perceived or actual dangerous threats.

- ✓ This mode of existence is emotionally and physically geared toward securing safety, removing risk, and responding to threat with forceful life-preserving and death-avoiding behavior.
- ✓ These involuntary mechanisms have evolved over tens of thousands of years—of running or hiding from predators, surviving and preparing for famine, and fighting threats to keep ourselves and our loved ones safe from harm or death.
- ✓ The sensitive response to apparent dangers, and preventative forecast of threat, has become so important to the survival of our species that this mode is activated even if the threat is simply suspected or perceived.
- ✓ Survival mode can be triggered even if you experience something as simple as the stress felt when facing a situation in life you feel challenged to handle.
- ✓ Danger doesn't have to actually exist.

Every single person that comes to me for help *fears her body*. She's afraid of what the body is, what it could be, what it isn't, and how others perceive it. To these clients, their body and the stigma of being overweight is their biggest threat and the biggest source of strain in their life. Whether she is trying to keep her body thin, fit, and healthy, or trying to get rid of fat, stop overeating, or prevent disease—her body is her biggest enemy. But it wasn't always that way. The relationship people have with their body isn't born in fear, shame, or hatred. How people relate to their body is something that is developed.

One of the first questions I ask clients when we initially talk is: *When did you first realize your body had a problem?*

Many of the clients who suffer from emotional or binge eating recall being compared to a family member. She was compared to her thinner sister, or compared to her obese relative who she was told had no willpower or self-control. Her body became an apparent threat, or a block, to her family's love and approval. Even if she met the praised body-image standards, if she internalized that approval, she became trapped by the pressure to maintain it.

Clients who are leaner or suffer from symptoms more like anorexia, often describe getting attention, reinforcement, and praise for how thin, fit, or beautiful she was—or others were. Regardless of the eventual strain with eating, dieting, and food, how the opinion of important family and friends mattered, and how they viewed hers and others' body, made a direct impact on how she related to her own body. These clients recall the first time their body went from something they never thought about, to something they had to be aware of every single day.

The relationship we have with our own body is the most sacred and intimate relationship of life. If you carry shame and fear of your body, you are likely to project this vulnerability into life.

The best way people know how to defend and protect themselves from this vulnerability is through weight-loss methods. Ultimately, the survival effort people project into food restrictions and weight loss triggers a reciprocal but counter-survival response to defend and protects one's access to food. They are stimulating survival mechanisms geared to preserve life through the required need for food.

Any person wanting to lose weight should examine:

1. How, in their mind, they came to the ideal body they are aspiring to achieve.
2. How that image in their mind makes them feel about their current body.
3. What they think that thinner body-image will do for their life.
4. What they think their current body is taking away from their life.
5. The symbolism they've attached to achieving the thinner body-image.
6. If they hope and want people to notice their body-image achievement.
7. If weight loss gives them a sense of freedom and safety to eat emotionally.
8. How food restrictions will feel once their weight loss is noticed.
9. How intense the pressure will be to achieve an even thinner body-image.
10. How that intensity pressurizes the need for them to further restrict food.
11. How they will feel if people notice they stop losing weight or if they regain weight.
12. How the pressure to be thinner and stay thin promotes increased perfectionistic dieting.
13. The way perfectionism makes small deviations seem catastrophic, increasing guilt, shame, and a sense of failure.
14. How the sense of failure with food restriction, impacts one's desire to eat food they've been restricting.

15. How their desire to eat impacts both their goal to lose weight and their current body.
16. How they will feel if they don't achieve the thinner body image.
17. What symbolism they've attached to themselves if they regain the weight.
18. How they would feel if others can see they've regained the weight.
19. How fear of regaining weight impacts the pressure to restrict more intensely once fat is lost.
20. How fear of regaining weight, and the intensified pressure to restrict food, impacts how they react to perceived imperfect eating.

SECTION 4

Why the HCG Diet can be Dangerous

A Client's Story

"My own story starts off as the oldest daughter from a strict religious family. I was my father's "favorite" and a lot of attention was put into me getting it "right." My days were often spent seeking my father's approval and doing things "perfectly.""

"I was in college when I started having issues around eating. I became bulimic and began the typical downward spiral. I suppose I had lingering issues with my body since that time, but my youthful joy to conquer the world kept it lying somewhat dormant in the background. I travelled out of the country quite a bit in my twenties until my first unplanned pregnancy, followed by some time as a single mother and the experience of being disowned by my father. After that was an unsuccessful marriage and child number two, followed by a brief stint of what appeared as happiness. Then, came my third unplanned pregnancy as an already single mother of two. Many said I "had father issues." It was at this point that I began to crash inwardly."

"As I struggled with depression and trying to make everything "right," I thought losing weight would give me a sense of control, and that's when I was introduced to the hCG protocol. I lost a large amount of weight, but something changed. I became more and more perfectionistic and obsessed with my weight and food. I started to binge uncontrollably knowing that I'd go back on the protocol, like it was my bulimic purge. Interestingly enough, I really didn't see it—what my real "problem" was."

"I called Robin for help after the first few days of learning about her. I was on hCG for about the seventh time because I thought maybe a diet would be "a good idea," to control my weight gains and emotional eating. I had already hit rock bottom, and in my suicidal state, I had basically abandoned my family a few weeks earlier and now was living three states away from my children."

"Before it all came crashing down, no one would have known anything was that wrong from my outward appearance. Everything looked picture perfect with me. I had spent years structuring my life around my perfectionistic ideas, and *I could no longer live in the hell I created for myself.* I did not know why or how I had gotten so low, but I desperately needed help."

Chapter 9

When Access to Food is Life or Death

"Fear doesn't exist anywhere except in the mind."
— Dale Carnegie, author

The Wolf in Sheep's Clothing

The vast majority of all people trying to achieve a more "superior" thinner body are failing, yet generation after generation we haven't recognized that this is an indication that the goal, and the means to achieve that goal, are unrealistic. Instead, people are directed to blame food, blame their lack of willpower, and to blame their body. Without recognizing that constant widespread failure is an indication the system isn't humanely realistic, it's understandable why the narcissistic dogma of thin supremacy has continued without question.

> **If the images being promoted as "normal" were required
> to reveal the likely achievability for the average individual,
> people could better understand how unnatural and
> inappropriate body-image and fitness standards are.**

With that knowledge:

- Consumers would know the truth about the unrelenting focus, effort, and permanent food restriction it would require to reach *and sustain* unrealistically high expectations.
- The idealistic body-image standards would lose their "superior" status and appeal.
- Consumers would quickly identify businesses trying to profit by selling such rubbish.
- People wouldn't so quickly judge themselves or others who struggle to achieve unrealistic expectations and standards.

However, the media selling weight loss and diets promote images as if it's easy and there's no alternative—in a way that the images and beliefs about thinness are seen as sacred truth coming from an authority with integrity that wants to help your "health." The ideals are promoted as if all "good" people should be able to reach them.

No one questions the validity and integrity of images that are promoted and sold as being easily reachable by an industry that profits from people feeling bad about their body. Without question, the weight-loss industry is given authority to define both what is the "right" body that provides a person with health, value, lovability, and worth, as well as the "right" way to restrict food to achieve this approval. Like totalitarian control, no one looks at the body-image belief system that's dictating *what the look is that you must achieve* as being dishonest and narcissistic, especially when there's been very little argument with the idea that being thinner is healthier.

To me, the concept of "healthy" attached to thinness is the wolf in sheep's clothing. People hold themselves to unrealistic body-image beliefs and food restrictions, thinking that it is healthier, when in fact many of the beliefs are radical, inhumane, and unachievable for most—unless they are willing to strain their mental and physical wellbeing. And instead of blaming the fantasy image as a narcissistic standard of insanity, the person suffering while attempting to achieve it gets labeled as "mentally unfit."

What if the expectation that anyone can reach these standards, even if they must perpetually starve themselves, is recognized as insane?

If the majority of followers generally suffer from low self-worth because of poor body image, and they end up with a dysfunctional relationship with food, disordered eating, or even an eating disorder, isn't this a reflection of the belief system and its strictness more so than being about the individuals who reinforce it?

But for many people, nobody is forcing them to follow radical body-image ideals. They personally hold themselves to it dogmatically, even when family, friends, and loved ones might be more loving, accepting, and lenient with what their body naturally is. In this case, the family isn't the reinforcing reason, but rather the individual is reinforcing a body image sold to her by a different relationship and the weight-loss industry. This is like a person who isn't raised in an overly religious environment, but who ends up joining a radical religious cult.

The HCG Diet Cult

When you look at the hCG diet industry as a weight-loss subculture—and how Dr. Simeons' protocol has been marketed emphasizing radically lean and fit bodies that promote the ultimate emotional goals of thin-supremacy—it's no wonder people often come out of it with worse emotional eating problems. Eventually when they regain any significant amount of weight they'd lost, they end up with a worse self-image than they had before. Failing at something as miraculous as the hCG protocol feels like a personal failure… but there's no one to blame.

The problem is that when the protocol is followed, 1) it typically results in rapid fat loss, 2) it results in significant size loss, and based on what I observed, 3) it significantly improves metabolic rates for people who are considered morbidly obese. You can read these findings in chapter 18 of *WLA-1*.

The hCG protocol not only appeals to people in terms of "health" benefits, but more so, it appeals as an emotional resolution for negative body image and the desperate need to "fit in" in order to be seen as acceptable in a thin-supremist culture.

Consequently, the relationship between the very-low calorie protocol and the effect of weight loss become extremely strained and pressurized, to the point that I've witnessed obsessive body-checking and explosive emotional and binge-eating behaviors as a result.

What I found is that the more underlying body-image strain a person had, the more likely she was to have increased cognitive distortions, all-or-nothing thinking, and the more her behavior and thoughts about food mimicked people in poverty. However, as participants who had less emotional needs for weight loss and less thin-supremacy beliefs, I observed that their emotional response to the exact same very-low calorie protocol was significantly different. They didn't show the same sensitivity to deprivation, emotional strain, and cognitive distortions about the weight loss and the food restrictions before, during, and after the very-low calorie protocol.

This observation brought me to ponder the influence survival mechanisms have on:
- People who are attracted to the hCG protocol as an emotional resolution for negative body image.
- How those survival mechanisms impact a participant's perceptions about food and eating restrictions during the very-low calorie protocol.

- If those survival mechanisms predispose participants to have cognitive distortions about the fat- and size-loss results of the protocol.
- If without those activated survival mechanisms, a participant's response to the very-low calorie protocol and the physical results were different.

The reason a person is attracted to and holds herself so tightly to radical cult ideals, like thin supremacy *as a way to survive*, is incredibly complex, and for the person living it, it is very difficult to understand. There are unseen forces, unquestioned beliefs, and possible trauma supporting her drive to harm her life with inhumane dieting concepts, in order to survive. There are perceived threats that make starvation seem "healthy" and dieting seem virtuous. For this reason, people might be attracted to radical food restrictions like Dr. Simeons' hCG protocol as a way to seek protection from perceived threats to her survival needs in order to feel worthy of inclusion.

Evolutionary Psychology and Maslow's Hierarchy of Survival Needs

According to *Oxford Living Dictionary,* a "threat" is a person or thing likely to cause damage or danger, or the *possibility* of trouble, danger, or ruin. The keywords here are "likely" and "possibility." Threat doesn't have to be guaranteed to create a biological response in the body. It only has to be a *perceived possibility*, which means any threat you think could happen can trigger a degree of survival mode.

> **It's as if the brain has a "danger probe" attached to it,
> like an invisible antenna that is geared to seek
> what you think you can't handle, and to detect
> vulnerability or potential danger.**

This probe magnifies and surveys the environment, people, their body language, and any situation, animal, or bug that memory has recorded "as dangerous."

Perceptions of threat promote the physical mechanisms necessary to react to that stress, whether it's to freeze in panic, hide in insecurity, or fight in self-defense. Even if there is no actual danger or risk, the feeling of insecurity can trigger this response. Our perceptions have a physical impact, and survival mode consequently impacts our perceptions.

When looking at fight, flight, or freeze, and the mechanisms of survival mode, this response is directly promoted by the fundamentals of evolutionary human psychology. *Evolutionary psychology* is based around the notion that throughout past ages, as humans have evolved physically to survive the environment, we have also evolved psychologically. *The foundation of our psychological wiring is based on the need, drive, and desire to survive—to stay alive and to avoid death.* It would make sense that our minds are pre-wired to be attracted to and defensive of necessary life needs, like food, water, and shelter.

One of the most renowned scientists who studied this type of human moti-

MASLOW'S HIERARCHY OF NEEDS

vation and behavior was Dr. Abraham Maslow (1908–1970). His pivotal work described our fundamental psychological drives being based on securing the most important life-and-death needs. Dr. Maslow is best known for what is called the "hierarchy of needs." He believed that before anything else, our mind is driven to first secure and to make safe the most important fundamental needs of life and survival, and once those needs are secure, then our mind prioritizes the next less-important survival needs.

We are wired to be highly sensitive to any perceptions of threat to those life needs. Cognitive distortions play an important role in how our mind shifts when we perceive apparent threat. However, once our fundamental survival needs are met, and we feel we have adequate capacity to handle potential threats, our mind shifts, and we are energized and motivated to be more exploratory and take more risks. Exploration, innovation, and expansion of knowledge through curiosity become a joy in life as the potential of the human race can expand.

As fear relaxes, then the body relaxes and, consequently, so do the survival-mode impulses and cognitive distortions that make so many people's lives miserable.

The idea is that by securing your most important survival needs, your mind opens, the way you function in life evolves, and you'll have confidence to explore and expand your experience in life, without feelings of inadequacy.

I believe this is the mirage many people are chasing when they set out to be thinner, and what they envision in their mind when they fantasize about what a weight-loss program—like the hCG diet—will provide them emotionally. They assume that being thinner will allow them the safety and security to open themselves up to experience the life they want. Unfortunately, I've never met someone who takes pride in her thinner body and thin supremacy who has this type of freedom. The problem is that weight loss typically requires a form of food restriction, and evolutionary wise, dieting might trigger a threat response to the most basic and important primitive survival need: food.

With fat loss, you might feel better about "fitting in,"
but your relationship with dieting and food gets
more strained and intense.

Survival and Food

The fundamental and most sensitive needs of survival are the most important requirements necessary physiologically in order to support the life of the body: food, water, clean air, sleep, etc. If these needs are threatened, insecure, or are not met, not only will you show signs of psychological stress, but also the physical stress without resolution eventually ends in death. As depicted in Maslow's Pyramid of Needs, our mind involuntarily prioritizes focus, and magnifies the desire for these requirements if they are perceived as threatened.

Considering the extreme food restrictive nature
of Dr. Simeons' 500-calorie hCG protocol, it's
fair to assume that participants are at high
risk for triggering the most sensitive survival
mechanisms geared specifically to
secure one's access to food.

If access to food is *perceived* to be threatened, the mind pushes less-important needs into the background, and brings forward all attention, motivation, and harnessed energy towards adequately securing these most important physical needs—to *above all else,* stay alive.

For example, if your food supply does not give you enough to eat today, cannot be replenished, or if it is perceived not safe to eat, the mind will devote attention to and emphasize what needs to be done to secure it. It will magnify attention on what tools are necessary to find food for immediate and later needs, places to forage and hunt, and how to stockpile enough food so the mind can be released to prioritize other less-important needs.

It's obvious to me that people who struggle with emotional eating and binge eating might be experiencing symptoms of this hierarchy of need—*not feeling secure.* If food supply is being threatened, you could say the mind will obsess to some degree on what it takes to secure food to make it:

— Available now,
— Adequate in quantity to support immediate needs,
— Safe to eat,
— Replenishable and stockpiled, and
— Good to taste.

This is described in more detail in *Hierarchy of Food Needs*, by Registered Dietician, Elly Satter, MS, RD, LCSW, BCD. Satter detailed what needs must be met in order to secure this hierarchy of need. Until food is fully and completely secure, the mind will need to keep thoughts of food and eating at the front of the mind *at all times.* It's as if your food is being threatened, and the mind's eye must keep constant watch over it.[14] Your mind will fight for you to get food, and this is experienced through urges, thoughts, cravings, hunger pains, and fantasies about food.

Ask yourself:

☐ Have you noticed that when you feel bad about your weight, your urges to overeat increase?

☐ When you feel bad about your body, do you feel pressure to restrict food, even when you know you aren't prepared or ready to diet?

☐ When you feel bad about your weight, do you feel bad when you eat?

☐ When you commit to a diet, have you noticed that your urge to overeat increases?

☐ While adhering to a food restriction, do you have to remove food from your home and avoid social events in order to keep your mind off food?

☐ When you are restricting food, do you find that you can't stop thinking about food, and are constantly thinking about when you get to eat next?

☐ When you are restricting, have you noticed that micro-managing, counting, charting, and controlling every detail of your food intake, as well as the timing of when you eat, helps repress the strong urges to eat?

☐ If you aren't under strict controls with your diet, do you feel out of control with food?

☐ When you've reached your weight-loss goals, do you feel an intense break in the pressure between you and food, like the floodgates have opened, and do you start overeating with careless abandon?

When you consider that roughly 97 million people in the United States diet, are preparing to diet, are just getting off of a diet, and that even more people don't diet, but think they should, that's a lot of people who are potentially triggering survival needs to securet heir access to food.[15]

The idea that access to food *might* be threatened or is forecasted to be scarce, can trigger the urge to get food in self-defense. This is one of the most important physiological and psychological needs, which makes sense for why people feel impelled to overeat the food they intend to restrict before and after the next diet—and why people with eating disorders describe being obsessed with every aspect of food.

It doesn't help when the weight-loss industry bombards consumers with con-stant propaganda that food is unsafe, toxic, causes cancer and other diseases, and is "bad" for you. Headlines such as "5 Foods You Should Never Feed Your

Children" or "5 Toxic Foods You Should Know About" promote fear that food is unsafe, again creating insecurity to the foundation of psychological well-being. This is why it is common for people that are not secure with food to rely heavily on nutritional messaging on food packaging, as an unconscious way to ease survival mechanisms that have been inflamed by their fear that food is unsafe to eat.

**Because of the vital requirement for our physiological
needs, particularly food, our psychological mind
is highly sensitive to perceptions of threat,
especially perceived famine.**

The amount of food we have, its availability, the ability to replenish food, and if we have enough for our family, is a primitive mechanism that has maintained animal life for tens of thousands of years. When there is lack of food, and the body experiences starvation, it's likely that our body, mind, motivation, and behavior will become focused and preoccupied on food. Consider the psychological and physiological impact when people voluntarily diet, especially when surrounded by food.

When it is perceived that food is abundant from every angle, including security from future dieting—only then does the work, stress, continuous contemplation, comparative deprivation, and worry that food isn't safe or won't be available start to diminish. It is at this point that the mind can take focus away from food, and onto other things. And even then, when hunger arises, it's difficult to function when symptoms of lightheadedness, fatigue, agitation and irritability associated with hunger shows up. Once food is readily available, safe to eat, adequate in quantity, and secure for the future, the mind shifts to other priorities.

However, even if food is abundant from every angle, the idea that access to food is threatened can trigger defense mechanisms. You can restrict food while be surrounded by it in abundance, and still have these survival impulses to feast. This was demonstrated in a famous scientific study performed: the Minnesota Starvation Project.

Chapter 10

An Experiment with Starvation

*"I just don't have the desire to do the things
I should do or the things I want to do."*
– Participant in the Minnesota Starvation Experiment

As I've monitored thousands of rounds of Dr. Simeons' hCG protocol, I've come to also observe how that many people respond emotionally to radically restricting food. Over time, I've learned to prepare people in a way to minimize their perceptions of deprivation, as to minimize the risk of triggering survival urges to eat and prevent them from deviating from the strict regulations of the very-low calorie protocol. Even if participants were emotionally detached from the weight and size-loss results, and didn't show signs of hormonal starvation like hunger pains or energy loss that you'd expect from a very-low calorie protocol, *I still observed symptoms that mimicked starvation in different ways.*

I observed that participant's taste and pleasure response to food was magnified in such a way that they described bland protocol food as delicious and euphoric. People described having a stronger sense of smell and having dreams of food.

Some of these symptoms undoubtedly resemble physical and psychological aspects of being starved of a variety of pleasures that's available when there's access to a diverse range of food.

I also observed certain psychological symptoms of starvation that would occur if a person is surrounded by food, specifically deprivation and perceptions of being punished or withheld from eating. These symptoms reminded me of the world-renowned Minnesota Starvation Experiment, done in 1944–1945 during World War II.

University of Minnesota Starvation Experiment

Thirty-sex men were selected and volunteered to undergo a 13-month starvation experiment where scientists studied the mental, physical, and social effects of food restriction, while being surrounded with food. This study was called the *Minnesota Starvation Experiment.* Initial findings were published in *Men and Hunger: A Psychological Manual for Relief Workers,* by Ancel Keys.

Keys, one of the most important researchers in the field of nutrition, was inspired to understand and better respond to the physical and psychological suffering that occurred while people were starved in concentration camps. When World War II finally ended, one of his goals was to study how starvation, or semi-starvation, changes motivation, behavior, intellect, emotions, and social engagement.

The experiment's volunteers were to walk 22 miles each week, had daily work assignments, and were required to keep a diary. The only restrictions in their life was with food. They were free to continue to live their social lives as normal. Their food intake for three months started around 3,200 calories a day. Then they spent another six months eating about 1,600 calories a day, which was half the amount of food they ate during the first phase.

During the semi-starvation phase (1,600 calories), scientists observed an instant decline in energy and personal motivation, noting apathy, and irrational irritability. Many subjects developed strange eating habits, like handling food as if it was "precious gold." They observed eating rituals such a licking the plates, extending out mealtime, putting water in their food to dilute it and make it last longer, or even holding bites of food in their mouths for a longer time before swallowing. Food became a source of fantasy and motivation. Many men became obsessive about collecting recipes, and food became a central topic of daydreams, cravings, and desires. One participant journaled, *"Stayed up until 5:00 a.m. last night studying cookbooks. They are so absorbing I can't stay away from them."*

Men drank excessive amounts of water seeking to feel full, some took up smoking to reduce hunger pain, and others chewed gum, sometimes up to 30 pieces a day. They eventually banned gum from the experiment.

> **NOTE:** *I find this observation fascinating since I have worked with at least a dozen participants who frequently binged on gum while on Dr. Simeons' very-low calorie protocol. Many of these descriptions of over drinking water, diluting food, and smoking to reduce hunger are also typical for people when they chronically diet.*

The researchers noticed dramatic changes in social motivation. They noted stagnation in the desire for personal development and relationships, and sexual desire significantly diminished. Social settings seemed exhaustive, and pointless, and many participants didn't want to talk to other people. In general, the men preferred to be alone, went to movies by themselves, and even if they found something entertaining, they didn't have the energy to laugh or enjoy it. When out in public they were passive, slower, and were easy to push around.

> **NOTE:** *I clearly remember feeling this way when I suffered with anorexic tendencies. However, these observations are counter to what*

I've observed with people who are injecting hCG and eating less than 500 calories on the protocol. People typically describe increased sex drive, improved energy, motivation to clean, and the urge to "nest" or purge excessive clothes and household goods. I assume these are symptoms directly linked to how hCG influences the endocrine system.

Although, the more hCG protocol participants felt emotionally strained with victim views of being punished or deprived of food, the more agitation and anger they had in environments where they were surrounded by the sight and smells of food they couldn't eat. This made them less motivated to socialize, like going to the movies where eating popcorn and candy are obvious deviations from the protocol.

Sometimes the men in the starvation experiment would experience moments of inexplicable euphoria, but with intense emotional crashes.

NOTE: *This sounds very similar to how I felt when I starved myself, and how others who suffer with anorexia also describe feeling— especially the euphoria attached to controlling hunger pangs.*

I've witnessed this euphoria with people who feel intense emotional relief with weight loss. These are the hCG protocol participants that come to the process with more intense goals based in thin supremacy.

One individual was removed from the project because he was sneaking food that wasn't permitted when he'd go into town. He described a "high" he'd get eating food that was off-plan, and admitted he stopped at 17 soda shops one time on his way home. He reported being so happy and elated, and he felt the world was a beautiful place. But following his cheating, he was downtrodden and would have a period of pessimism and regret, and he felt like a failure for not being able to stay on the reduced rations.

NOTE: *This reminds me of the excitement to binge, and the resulting shame many binge eaters feel, including myself, after not being able to follow a restrictive diet plan.*

> **It's very exciting to know you're going to have a small window of opportunity to eat without feeling bad about it—until it's over, because then the remorse and self-deprecation is very intense.**

Again, this is more common with people who feel punished and deprived of food emotionally during the very-low calorie protocol. When perspective changes, these tendencies disappear.

I assume this binge-eating euphoria and behavior is oriented as a self-preserving survival mechanism—like fighting and winning a competition in order to temporarily get access to food. But afterward, you feel bad because you did believe doing so is wrong or is an indication you are bad because you couldn't handle the deprivation.

When the University's 20-week semi-starvation phase was over, the participants went through a food reintegration and rehabilitation phase. As they physically recovered, they still had lingering mental consequences. Plate licking continued, irritability became aggression when it came time to eat, and the participants' mood swings were more severe. It took three months for their mood and social behavior to even out and normalize. Surprisingly, the researchers found that the men needed as much as 4,000 calories a day to reduce the sensation of hunger during the reintegration phase.

The main scientist, Ancel Keys, convinced twelve of the participants to stay on at the lab for another eight weeks. He wanted to continue to monitor them during an "unrestricted rehabilitation" phase. Left to their own devices, Keys observed these men consume over an average of 5,000 calories a day. In some cases, some of them ate as many as 11,500 calories in a single day. One man was hospitalized for several days because he'd eaten so much; thus he needed his stomach pumped. For many months, the men reported having a desire to eat that they could not satisfy, no matter how much they ate.

> *NOTE: This is counter to what I've observed as people transition off the very-low calorie protocol on the first phase, to the low-carb low-starch second phase of the protocol. This could be due to the hormonal influence hCG has on leptin, making hunger pains less of a problem. Also, I believe teaching participants to eat based on hunger rhythms that guide when and how much to eat before, during, and after the protocol minimizes perceptions of loss, punishment, and deprivation during and after the very-low calorie protocol.*
>
> *However, people who were more emotional about weight loss and held themselves more intensely to thin-supremist beliefs, had more emotional stress with the restrictions, and felt punished and deprived of food. As a result, they had a more emotional response after the very-low calorie protocol impelling them to overeat. They often "lose control" once the restrictions are removed.*

However, the study found that the men's bodies returned to perfect health after a few months of consistent re-feeding. Some men in the experiment did gain back more weight than they had before. They gained back their original weight plus about 10 percent. But over the following six months their weight gradually declined as their satiation for food normalized, and they did not restrict again. By the end of the follow-up period, they were approaching their pre-experiment weight and fat levels.

The body can safely survive starvation and reintroduction to food. But the mind doesn't so quickly relax psychologically. There might be another threat to one's access to food around the corner.

When There's Multiple "Starvation Experiments"

The Minnesota Starvation Experiment was instrumental in helping scientists get a better understanding of how the mind and body responds to forced famine. However, for this research to be relevant to how dieting works, the participants would've had to intermittently do the starvation experiment multiple times, over and over again. Imagine how the participants would have responded if they knew they were going to have to do the experiment again and again and again, with a two-to-three month break in between.

- Would their eating have normalized the same way if they knew they were going to have to starve again in the near future?
- Would they have shown signs of emotional eating or binge eating prior to starting the next food restriction phase?
- What type of foods would they overeat prior to the next starvation period?
- What is the likelihood that they'd follow the restrictions the second, third, fourth, or fifth time they were starving themselves?
- Would binge-eating behavior increase as more and more starvation experiments are done?

In 2003, 18 survivors of the original 36 volunteers were interviewed as part of an oral history project about the experiment. They described that there had been some lingering aftereffects of the experiment. For many years, they were haunted by a fear that food might be taken away from them again. Imagine the impact on their psychological and physical wellbeing if the experiment was repeated over and over again, for years and years, *like chronic dieting does for tens of millions of people today.*

- As they fatigue, would they justify cheating on the experiment when they had emotional distress, social functions, or experienced increased hunger or cravings?

- What would happen if the starvation experiment included a competition of who lost more body fat, who became the thinnest, and who was deemed more "attractive" after losing weight?
- Would they feel bad about regaining weight during their rest period?
- With this "who's thinner" competition, how would the larger-sized participants respond when they are viewed as lazy, incompetent, not wanting it enough, or weak and lacking self-control?
- Would they gain more and more weight with each rest period between each starvation experiment?
- Would their body ever go back to its prior original size and weight, after years of repeated under- and over-eating?

When you think about what the men experienced in their one-time starvation experiment, it seems harsh.

But when you look at multiple generations of people voluntarily submitting themselves to starvation diets, over and over and over again—for the sake of trying to prove they are good and worthy people— the cruelty of it all is more obvious.

And the mental health issues in relation to food make complete sense. A person who chronically diets will predictably have stress and anxiety about her weight, as well as the reality that with weight gain comes another "starvation experiment." The truth of the matter is that people have been experimented on for decades, as "new and improved" diets have been released constantly for nearly a century. For some people, the repeated attempt to restrict food has been with them for most of their life. It's not surprising to me when I work with people who've chronically been on and off diets that they have symptoms that look like Post Traumatic Stress Disorder (PTSD). This makes we wonder if binge eating is a symptom of "Diet PTSD."

Diet PTSD

Many clients I work with often experience intense panic if they think food is going away. Despite the weight they gain consistently overeating, it seems as if they are running away from food restrictions, as if they're running from a "diet predator." Part of the problem is that over time they've developed a reliance on eating in order to cope when emotionally challenged, but they also overeat because it seems that they'll have to starve the rest of their life to lose the weight they've gained.

> **I believe impulses to overeat in anticipation
> of future food deprivation is a significant
> reason why binge eating, or emotional
> eating, is so common for people who
> chronically diet.**

The stress a person has about her weight and health isn't important when she believes the next diet will fix everything, as she emotionally eats in preparation to deprive herself of food. And the longer she plans to restrict eating, the more intense her mind suggests she fight for access to food. She becomes "obsessed" as the urge to eat takes over her motivation and mind. Ultimately, the famine she eventually anticipates gets longer and stricter with each binge and with each pound of fat she gains.

Ask yourself:
> **After dieting and losing weight, have you been impelled
> to overeat and accepted weight gain, thinking the next
> diet or round of the hCG protocol will help you
> 1) get back on track? Or 2) will help you re-lose
> the weight you're about to re-gain?**

The Minnesota Starvation Experiment provides a great example of how motivation and energy adapt when access to food is reduced. It also confirmed what Abraham Maslow had theorized in his pyramid describing our survival "Hierarchy of Needs." The mind will fixate on securing more important needs for life, such as food, until that need is secure both physically and psychologically.

> **It doesn't matter if you are starving because of true famine, a six-month scientific starvation experiment, or a 30-day cleanse, the body and mind evolved to respond to perceptions of deprivation in a way that preserves life—*no matter what.***

However, if you were to compare a person who is subject to a true famine where food isn't easily accessible—would they respond differently than a person who is food restricted, but surrounded by large amounts of accessible food?

Of course, feasting, stocking, and preserving food would be vital when preparing for famine. But if the famine is artificial, meaning it is contrived as food is in fact abundant and accessible, how would these urges impact a person's impulsivity to eat? This is an important question when preparing people for any form of dieting, especially something as severe as the 500-calorie hCG protocol. *How do you help keep people from not experiencing the impulses to feast before and after the artificial famine when access to food is abundant and perpetually available?*

Artificial Famine and the Impulse to Binge

Obviously, most of the strain people feel when restricting food is increased hunger. But even without hunger, a huge amount of strain is connected to having to restrict while surrounded by food, and also when experiencing emotions that food normally fulfills. Another strain is being around others who are eating food that you're restricting, or when the taste and quantity of food you get to eat is lacking.

While there's easy access to large quantities of food, forecasted deprivation increases the likelihood you'll eat excessively.

A victim-based perception of food being unfairly withheld triggers more desire, more cravings, and more food-seeking behavior as mechanisms of self-defense. In studies comparing dieters who are around forbidden food, compared to dieters removed from access to forbidden food, there was an increase in feelings of deprivation, cravings, and binge eating behavior after food was reintroduced.[16]

According to research that investigated neuro adaptations to food scarcity as it concerns binge eating, Psychologist Dr. Kenneth Carr said:

> "Weight-loss dieting amidst an abundance of supranormally re-warding foods and cues signaling their availability is likely to be stressful, and inevitably lead to episodes of loss of control."

He suggests that such episodes of food restriction while being surrounded by highly palatable foods could be hazardous as it contributes to binge pathology.[17] This means that when you restrict a favorite food like pizza, when you see and smell the aroma of pizza as others around you eat it, you are going to feel deprived, resulting in a strong urge and impulse to overeat pizza.

If you were to experience famine where food is scarce all around, you are less likely to feel sorry for yourself, or feel deprived, because you can do nothing about it. However, if you are restricted from food (for superficial reasons, like trying to fit into a dress), and palatable food is abundant around you, where you can see, smell, and watch others eat, the impulse to overeat will be significantly stronger.[16]

Restriction and Deprivation

Feelings of *deprivation* stem from perceptions of food being withheld from you. This emotion is very different than *restriction,* because deprivation puts a person in the position of being a victim, or in a state of poverty in the mind relative to available food that is abundant. It feels like you could eat, but you're not allowed to—that everyone else gets to enjoy food, but not you. *Deprivation* is a feeling of being withheld, especially if you feel you are entitled or deserve it.

Restriction is a limitation, but it isn't necessarily an affront like poverty surrounded by abundance. You can imagine that when a person restricts food and then feels deprived, they are more likely to overeat to compensate for the perceived "unfairness" or entitlement. In a way, deprivation is a form of defense, or self-preservation. You are fighting for your right to eat, when that right seems to have been taken away from you from an outside force.

I often see *deprivation* come up when a person wants the emotional benefits of weight loss, and she strictly controls her food (like during the very-low calorie protocol), but her body doesn't lose the amount of weight she thought she deserved. In this case, the reward for enduring the survival strain with food didn't provide the desired results, and what comes up in self-defense is anger and the impulse to eat in order to make things "even."

> **Clearly the more strain a person feels when she's**
> **restricting food, the more sensitivity to feeling**
> **deprived she'll have if she isn't rewarded equally.**

Even if there's sufficiently rewarded weight loss, the strain of food restrictions on survival needs can be intense enough that successful weight loss can be used as a reason to release oneself from the diet restraint in order to fulfill needs with food. Weight loss is a bargaining tool to justify access to unrestrained eating.

"Addiction" to Food

Furthermore, your brain's dopamine response to food strengthens after palatable food has been restricted.[16] This means that the more you restrict a certain type of food and then feel deprived, the brain is more sensitive to pleasure when that food is reintroduced. This could be why the patients in the Minnesota Starvation Experiment, as well as the people I observed on the hCG 500-calorie protocol thought the bland, flavorless food they were served during the semi-starvation phase was delicious. Additionally, as people hold in mind the food they crave, desire for that food increases, especially when the food in mind has been restricted.[17]

The desire to eat is strongest for people who feel deprived because they are surrounded by a variety of food they want but can't eat.

Even if you have access to an abundance of food, but restrict certain types of food that you enjoy, it has been shown you will more than likely experience desire and cravings for that specific food, even if you aren't hungry.[17]

Studies suggest that when trying to restrict a certain food group or type of food, a paradox is created by an increased need to be aware of the "bad" food that has shown to increase a desired state for that food. In *The Psychology of Food Craving: Symposium on "Molecular mechanisms and psychology of food intake,"* obesity expert and professor of Sports and Exercise Science, Andrew Hills states, "In the context of food and eating, there are circumstances in which trying to distract oneself from thinking about a particular desired food makes evidence of the existence and appeal of that food more prominent."[17]

This is commonly experienced: when people try to restrict candy, they inadvertently think about candy more often than they would if they weren't restricting.

The reasons why we restrict food and how much time we are removed from food, can change how our food-preserving survival mechanisms respond. It's a matter of changing the context for why you are restricting food. Studies have shown that when food is voluntarily and temporarily restricted for a more heartfelt reason, such as a spiritual fast, the cravings and desire to eat do diminish, and the occurrence of overeating afterward is much less. The same goes for people who can't eat food to which their body has an anaphylactic/sensitivity/allergic reaction—or in situations of famine where everyone around you can't eat either.

When there is a more profound reason to temporarily reduce food intake as a choice, the risk of perceiving the restrictions as deprivation greatly reduce, and as a result the likelihood diminishes that a person will trigger mechanisms that drive the urge to eat in self-defense.

For example, the men who volunteered for the Minnesota Starvation Experiment did so as a way to improve the health care of people who were recovering from being held in concentration camps in Europe. Imagine having done the starvation experiment for a different reason—like as a way to prove your worth through the discipline required to handle food restrictions, and to repress the psychological strain that occurs when being deprived. You can imagine that in comparison eating behaviors and motivations would be different.

When preparing people for Dr. Simeons' hCG protocol, I make them aware of the risks of feeling deprived, and the survival mechanisms that could get triggered while reinforcing the 500-calorie protocol. If the intent of doing the protocol is strictly physical as a medical therapy, they are less likely to feel deprived and victimized by the temporary restrictions.

However, if their goals are based on the *vanity of thin supremacy,* the likelihood that they'll finish the protocol is less, and the chances they'll diet once the very-low calorie protocol is over, is extremely high. This basically guarantees any physical rehabilitation that occurred as a result of the protocol will be reversed, and the cycle of dieting and emotional eating will continue—especially if the participants fear weight gain afterward, and that fear projects onto food as if food is a threat. There are physical reactions to fear that might reverse any healing benefits of the hCG protocol.

Chapter 11

How Fear of Food Affects the Body

"Malice literally makes us sick; we are always the victims of our own vindictiveness. Even secret hostile thoughts result in a physiological attack on one's own body."
– Dr. David R. Hawkins, PhD, Psychiatrist and world-renowned spiritual guru

Fight or Flight

All of the people I work with are adults, typically ranging in age from 25–65 years old. On occasion I've had clients in their late teens or even in their 70s Most people who've sought out my help started fearing food and worrying about their weight in adolescence, so by the time they reach out to me for help, they've been suffering for at least a decade. That means their body has been in stress mode with food, in some cases, for over 20, 30, or even 40 years. These people are chronic sufferers, and that ultimately comes with chronic physical symptoms.

One of the most interesting observations I've made while working with hundreds and hundreds of people from the entire spectrum of eating disorders, is that many of these people have similar physiological ailments. There are long lists of dangerous health consequences I believe stem from chronic dieting and overeating, and the stress connected to both.

I am going to focus specifically on issues stemming from perceptions of fear and survival mode.

Besides the obvious cognitive struggles like anxiety, obsessive and compulsiveness, and depression, many of the people I've worked with struggle with a variety of problems like digestive ailments, osteoporosis, low thyroid, autoimmune disorders like Hashimotos, and Polycystic Ovarian Syndrome (PCOS). These issues could be genetic, environmental, or a consequence of daily living in stress for a long period of time about their body and around food. *However, eating disorders can affect every organ system in the body, and people struggling with an eating disorder need to seek medical and professional help.*

When seeking answers to why I commonly observe certain ailments, I decided to look at fear and the possibility that the anxiety experienced every time a person ate might have physiological consequences. I wondered if fear of the body and food might be enhancing these client's health issues. Why do they all seem to have digestive problems, slower thyroid, and sensitivity to high blood sugar no matter what their weight? To keep this book from getting too academic, I will summarize what I found.

Digestion and Fear

In a sea of research articles, every study I found referenced Dr. Walter Cannon, the "king" of physiology. In the first chapter of Dr. Cannon's book, *Bodily Changes in Pain, Hunger, and Rage*, he discusses the emotions of fear and anger, and how they impact digestion.

He goes into great detail describing the observations of other physiologists, like

Ivan Pavlov, regarding the impact that fear, anger, and other excitement emotions have on salivation, stomach fluids, and digestion. Dr. Cannon describes:

> *"The conditions favorable to proper digestion are wholly abolished when unpleasant feelings such as vexation and worry and anxiety, or great emotions such as anger and fear, are allowed to prevail... The influences unfavorable to digestion, however, are stronger than those which promote it. And evidently, if the digestive process, because of emotional disturbance, is for some time inhibited, the swallowing of food which must lie stagnant in the stomach is a most irrational procedure. If a child has experienced an outburst of passion, it is well not to urge the taking of nourishment soon afterwards. Macbeth's advice that 'good digestion wait on appetite and health on both,' is now well-founded physiology."*

In his first chapter, Dr. Cannon writes specifically how important the physiology of pleasure is to salivation, gut "watering," and the overall digestibility of the body when the mind is at ease. He described findings from other scientists who found digestion improved with increased pleasure and excitement for food.

> *"Hornborg found that when the little boy whom he studied chewed agreeable food, a more or less active secretion of gastric juice invariably started, whereas the chewing of an indifferent substance, as gutta-percha, was followed by no secretion. All these observations clearly demonstrate that the normal flow of first digestive fluids, the saliva and the gastric juice, is favored by pleasurable feelings which accompany the taste and smell of food during mastication, or which are roused in anticipation of eating when choice morsels are seen or smelled... These facts are of fundamental importance in the serving of food."*

This information is exceedingly important as it can be related to people who chronically diet and live fearful of, and omit, pleasurable food. They keep away from social gatherings, remove food they enjoy, reduce tasteful dressings, and avoid other aspects of eating such as sharing food as a symbol of love and safety. People who diet are often afraid to eat "bad" food, to the point that they avoid plates and dishes, and are reluctant to relax around food. The reluctance to face food and relax with the pleasure of food could be a direct symptom of "fight-or-flight" Dr. Cannon describes in his book. This survival mode around food is incredibly relevant in response to digestion when observing the physical issues typical of chronic dieters, and of people with disordered eating or eating disorders.

Based on the science presented by Dr. Cannon, shaming and demonizing food, even threatening pleasurable food as addictive, could have unintended consequences harming the physical being of those who rigidly believe in dieting. Chronic dieters often describe having anxiety if they feel hunger, and they panic when around "bad" food.

I believe a discussion of how this fear of food impacts digestion and the body's ability to properly break down food is vitally important when observing common ailments of people who live by the safety of diets and fear of food.

Dr. Cannon describes in his first chapter:

> *"Like the peristaltic waves in the stomach, the peristalsis and the kneading movements (segmentation) in the small intestine, and the reversed peristalsis in the large intestine all cease whenever the observed animal shows signs of emotional excitement... There is no doubt that just as the secretory activity of the stomach is affected in a similar fashion in man and in lower animals, so likewise gastric and intestinal peristaltic waves are stopped in man as they are stopped in lower animals, by worry and anxiety and the stronger affective states."*

Peristalsis is the smooth muscle contractions of the stomach and small and large intestines that churns the food, helping break it down and push it through the intestines to later be excreted. Together with reduced secretion of digestive enzymes, when in fear, anxiety, worry, or anger, the mechanism of peristalsis shut down. To a dieter who fears food, this ensures poor and incomplete digestion.

> **Considering that the fear response completely shuts down digestion, if the source of threat, fear, and anxiety are negative beliefs about desired food a person wants to eat, it would be expected that the individual holding those fear-based beliefs would also have symptoms of poor digestion.**

Consider how chronic dieting and fearing "bad" food can impact digestion over a long period of time. When there are years and years of fearing food, you could predict that chronic dieters have symptoms associated with under-digested food dumping into the small intestines, gallbladder distress, poor nutritional absorption, and overall stress to the entire digestive tract.

Survival Mode and "Emotional" Blood Sugar

Another important connection dieting has to survival mode, or fight or flight, and disordered eating, is the fact that with fear and stress the body naturally secretes sugar into the blood stream. In chapter five of Dr. Cannon's book, *Bodily Changes in Pain, Hunger, Fear, and Rage,* he recognizes the impact that fear and stress have on blood sugar. It is believed the main reason for this mechanism is to make fuel readily available for the muscles in case of intense and prolonged demand that you must be very active, like having to run from a bear.

Cannon says:

> *"Great grief and prolonged anxiety during a momentous crisis have been regarded as causes of individual instances of diabetes, and anger*

or fright has been followed by an increase in the sugar excreted by the persons who already have the disease... In cases of mental disease, also, states of depression have been described accompanied by sugar in the urine... In these cases, the amount of glycosuria (glucose in urine) is dependent on the degree of depression, and that the greatest excretion of sugar occurs in the fear psychoses."

Personal Story: When I Had Diabetes

After filing bankruptcy and closing my business during the "depression" in 2008 timeline, my husband and I moved our family across the country from Idaho to Minnesota. This is where I published my first book, *Weight-Loss Apocalypse-1* in 2011. Over the span of seven years, because of my husband's job change, we ended up moving six times, and three of those moves were across the country. When we finally settled back in Idaho years later, we again had health insurance covered by my husband's employer. After I decided to get a blood panel done to check on my overall health, I received a phone call from the doctor's office, explaining that I had diabetes.

I am not considered overweight, I live an active lifestyle, and I don't emotionally eat, over-drink alcohol, or live in fear (I'll never do that again). I do not meet the typical associations to diabetes, in any way. However, it does run in my father's side of the family.

There was one other thing: I didn't tell the doctor that I had moved across the country three months prior. Or that I moved across the country six months before that, or that we moved nine months before that, and across the country 18 months before that. I didn't tell her that a year before that I filed bankruptcy and lost our home, and for over a year working over 70 hours a week, still struggled to feed my family. And to top it off, I didn't tell the doctor my mother was diagnosed with terminal brain cancer either.

I knew why I was diabetic: repeated bouts of intense stress. I knew what the

144

problem was, and chose to let my body come down from the stress. A year later, I had the doctor recheck my numbers, and I was perfectly normal and healthy.

Fear of Food and Blood Sugar

It would make sense then that a person with fear, stress, and anxiety about food would naturally have higher blood sugar before and after she eats. If she eats the food she's demonized as "bad," it would make sense that the body would have a magnified reaction to it.

In other words, if experiencing fear of food that's been eaten, the person would ultimately have a more-sensitive blood-sugar response to eating, which makes hermore susceptible to symptoms of higher blood sugar and weight gain.

This is not necessarily promoted by the quantity of food she eats, but rather promoted by the fear she experiences eating, or being around "bad" food. The combination of the two would certainly make her body more sensitive to weight gain than a person of equal size—who is not frightened or ashamed of eating.[18] Unfortunately, this blood-glucose sensitivity from the fear of food isn't associated with her anxiety about eating. Instead the blame is placed on the contents in the food, which perpetuates the fear and anxiety experienced when eating or being around that food.

Based on fundamental reactions to turned down, or down-regulated digestion, and turned up, or upregulated blood sugar when experiencing fear, you'd think the diet and health industry would stop demonizing food, but it seems that shaming food *is a source of revenue.* For people who internalize these fear-based beliefs about food, in regards to weight gain, they are going to experience higher levels of anxiety about food, and will be more sensitive to higher blood sugar and poor digestion when they eat it.[19] In this case, it is like a self-fulfilling prophecy where if you think that food is fattening, your body will then respond accordingly.

According to Dr. Cannon:

> *"If these results of emotion and pain are not 'worked off' by action, it is conceivable that the excessive adrenin and sugar in the blood may have pathological effects."*

He is suggesting that without exercise and physical labor that stress prepares the body for (running from a predator), the body will have to deal with the toxic excess of fuel that isn't balanced with activity. This excess fuel gets converted into glycerol, then into tri-glycerides, and eventually is stored as fuel. When stress is triggered in the brain, exercise can be a much-needed mental and physical relief. Unfortunately, studies have shown that people who feel bad about their weight are less motivated to exercise, in fear of being made fun of.[20] Over time the underutilized energy and fuel stimulated by stress might promote pathological effects like 1) a slower thyroid, 2) higher levels of testosterone in women, 3) increases in estrogen in men, 4) adrenal fatigue, and 5) obvious digestive issues and nutritional malabsorption.

If the individual has life circumstances, like job loss, a death in the family, or marital stress, this would exacerbate her magnified blood sugar and suppressed digestive response, on top of the shame and guilt that she experiences eating "dangerous" or bad food. And with these types of life stresses, a person who is "battling their weight" would have a more exaggerated response *because of her fear of food.*

Add to that a drop in physical activity due to injury or stress that renders her without the motivation, energy, or tolerance for physical activity, and the physiological sensitivity to weight gain heightens even further.

Instead of looking at the entire picture to understand the body's heightened sensitivity promoted by stress, both the diet and health industry incriminates the food. They say things like, *"That food is so bad for you. It's toxic, causes cancer, and it's fattening too. You'll end up with diabetes."* Shaming and distorting the facts to make it seem as if food is toxic no matter how much is eaten, carries the underlying belief that your body can't handle it.

When Your Body Can't Handle "Bad" Food

In effect, *the message that food is bad is also a message that your body can't handle it.* This type of fear mongering isn't only about food but it's also about the capacity of the body. From my observation, the result isn't rational abstinence of the feared food, but rather distrust and fear regarding the body's ability to handle and process food in a way that isn't threatening to its wellbeing. As a result, people not only fear food, but they fear their body's capacity to safely digest, process, and metabolize food. This promotes not just one but two sources of vulnerability. Not only is food toxic, but your body is also weak, broken, and too flawed to handle it.

Imagine being at the movie theatre, and the popcorn you were raised to enjoy is now considered "bad" because you're told your metabolism and hormones can't handle it. How are you going to feel when friends and family order popcorn for everyone—when you think your body can't handle eating it? If the popcorn was solely seen as bad, you might still enjoy some but choose to eat less. But when you add the belief that your body isn't capable of handling popcorn, it feels as if you are walking on eggshells. With just one bite, everything is ruined and there's no point to holding back.

> **Because the body is perceived to be too weak and broken to handle popcorn, one or two bites are seen as damaging. The belief your body isn't capable of "bad" food polarizes the choice to eat these foods as either all or nothing, especially when a person thinks she will restrict again later.**

When certain foods are believed to be disastrous for your body, it is assumed that the only way to have success is to restrict perfectly: *total abstinence.* Therefore eating "bad" food when it is believed your body can't handle it assumes even one bite causes damage. The common reactionary thought is that once those bites are taken and the damage is done, it isn't worth enforcing the strain of food restriction anymore if the benefits have been ruined. For many people, this is the tipping point of a binge or what some people call "emotional eating." *The combined impact of "bad" food and having a "bad" body isn't improved food restriction; it's increased risk of binge eating.*

When a person has more and more increased fear and anxiety about her body when she eats, the physical symptoms of fight-or-flight that Dr. Cannon observed would be more pronounced. In that state, imagine the physiological response as a person eats "bad" food. Besides the fact that she now feels shame and failure for eating that food, the all-or-nothing mentality simultaneously promotes binge eating while her body exhibits fight-or-flight physiology.

> **NOTE:** This is why I encourage a person to forgive herself instantly if she deviates from the hCG protocol restrictions. Forgiving yourself reduces the likelihood you'll cognitively distort your mistakes. You won't need to justify, reason, or negotiate with your guilt to continue breaking the protocol, and you're less likely to catastrophize the consequences, driving an all-or-nothing approach. One cookie on the protocol is most certainly not the same as eating five or ten more cookies, and feeling bad about it won't make anything better. Straining about it will make things emotionally and physically worse.

Because of the psychological stress, she'll have higher blood sugar before she starts eating, and while she's bingeing, her body isn't going to produce digestive enzymes, but it will stop digestive peristalsis for hours, and it will simultaneously release stress-and-fight hormones such as leptin, adrenaline, and cortisol. This person is most definitely going to have physical symptoms, especially if she doesn't effectively chew the food, which is true of most people during a binge.

Is it fair to blame food for physical reactions that might be due to primitive mechanisms meant for survival mode?

Many of my clients have suffered with poor body image, dieting, and emotional eating for years before being diagnosed with digestive problems, metabolic syndromes, and thyroid disorders. I ask clients if they've informed their doctors of their emotional issues with dieting and emotional eating, and virtually none of them have disclosed that information. In my opinion, it would be advantageous for these medical professionals to know how many of their patients suffer with disordered eating and eating disorders, and why that might be significant information as they seek answers and resolutions to these ailments—especially if the recommendations for the patient's ailments are food restrictions and weight loss. Food restrictions with the goal being body-image based, might actually be promoting their symptoms.

In these cases, with weight loss being an emotional goal, the hCG protocol would be more dangerous to their health than the excess body fat they are seeking to lose.

Chapter 12

Chasing the Thin-Supremacy Mirage

"Food shouldn't be what strengthens our emotions, and neither should weight reactively motivate the way we eat. Instead of relying on a diet to restrict eating, or the food industry to properly spoon-feed us, it's time we hold ourselves accountable as individuals."
— *Weight-Loss Apocalypse-1,* chapter 1 page 30

Our evolutionary psychology that is geared toward survival before all else is highly sensitive to our perceptions about access to food. Essentially, if food isn't perceived as safe, available, and abundant, the mind will continue to prioritize focusing on it until it is. Therefore, people who believe in dieting as a lifestyle tend to have more difficulty controlling their urges to overeat. And those urges confirm their belief that diets are necessary to control those urges. They are chasing their tail, going round and round in circles trying to limit food that is wired in the mind to magnify in importance when restricted.

Unfortunately, it's assumed by outsiders that as people struggle to curb these survival-mode impulses to eat that they are lazy, incapable, have no self-control, are dumb, can't handle it, or don't want to be thin enough when they eat. Most people don't look at either the restrictions, or the fear mongering of food, as major factors contributing to the problem.

Many binge eaters feel that by eating she has done something wrong. I've had many clients who felt any eating, even if it was "healthy" food, was bad. This alone threatens food because in order to feel better about it, she'd have to live perpetually restricted from *all food*. A person who regularly binges seems to relate to eating in a way that suggests her access to food is continuously being threatened.

The Unintended Consequences of Trying to Improve Body Image with the HCG Protocol

When someone internalizes a body image that requires chronic food deprivation, unfortunately unintended consequences can arise. In general, the idea behind most people's motivation to do the hCG protocol, or any diet, is that the weight loss will be so defining that it will unlock a sense of confidence, allowing her the freedom to explore life. This makes it seem that the reward for losing weight will be so beneficial that the strain and discomfort of dieting will be worth it. However, this doesn't take into account the fact that restricting food comes with both emotional strain and discomfort that magnifies and increases the longer a person diets.

**Even if the hCG prevents hormonal symptoms of
starvation during the very-low calorie protocol,
psychological symptoms can increase
the longer a person reinforces it.**

The problem is that human capacity to sustain and control "forced famine" is meant only to be temporary. Our bodies have to eat to adequately sustain life, and we aren't wired to emotionally and physically accept permanent scarcity. Agitating psychological survival mechanisms—to think about, seek, find, and eat food—increase and magnify in intensity the longer a person deprives. This deprivation creates a conundrum between:

- Food-restrictive lifestyle it takes for people to lose fat while surrounded by abundant amounts of food,
- The evolved psychological mechanisms that progressively increase motivation to eat the longer those restrictions are applied, and
- The challenge to sustain fat loss while experiencing stress and mental fixation on food.

When a person sets out to lose weight to improve body image, and the motivation to restrict seems tolerable, she isn't taking into account the fact that the ease of restrictions in the beginning is going to feel far more challenging the longer she diets and the more weight she loses. In order to sustain the diet, the "work" to restrict food becomes unrealistic against the awakened primitive survival mechanisms to preserve life with food.

At some point the food restrictions will need to go away, and with the protocol, that is the case. As people transition from the very low-calorie protocol into the second phase, fats and more diversity in food need to be reintroduced. Once those three weeks are over, participants are to reintegrate access to all diversity of food available. The only way to understand how the hCG protocol worked for the body is to observe how the body responds to eating like normal, without food restrictions. How the body responds over time in comparison to how it responded prior to the hCG protocol is the best way to understand if there were any significant therapeutic effect.

However, if the participant is emotionally attached to the weight-loss results of the very low-calorie protocol, following the protocol when it requires increased food intake and food diversity can feel threatening.

With regular dieting, the restrictions and sacrifices that a person made to be thinner are meant to remain in focus to stay thinner. *The hCG protocol is not meant to be approached that way.* Just because a person experiences significant size and fat loss during the very low-calorie protocol, doesn't mean she should continue the very low-calorie protocol when it's over in order to maintain those changes. More food and more diverse choices must be reintroduced!

As the participant stops injecting the hCG, experiences increased hunger, and is allowed more diversity in food, her fear of weight regain can result in anxiety about eating and the urge to continue restricting food in order to hold onto the very low-calorie results. Even though the protocol directs otherwise, people often choose to break the protocol by continuing to restrict and this comes with urges to overeat for which they might not be prepared. This conundrum between wanting to maintain weight loss, dieting, and increasing urges to eat is extremely confusing.

Weight loss that a person thought would give her access to the freedom of life actually traps her in an intense game of all or nothing thinking. On one hand she secures food and fails her body-image goal, or on the other hand she reaches her goal but lives with intense obsessiveness and focus on food. It's like a doubled-edged sword that protects her on one side, and harms her on the other.

For this reason, in order for the protocol to be approached and followed as it is prescribed specifically as a medical treatment for hormonal imbalances, it is important that participants let go of expectations attached to body image so that they are less likely to diet in fear once the very low-calorie phase of the protocol is over. They must be willing to accept weight gain and the truth of how the protocol might or might not have rehabilitated their metabolism and hormonal imbalances.

Chasing the Mirage of Thin Supremacy

It's very rare to come across someone who lost weight once, as if it was a destination, and felt complete and satisfied with that one-time achievement. *The idea behind body image is that your body must stay that way.*

In reality, dieting to stay thin is a marathon that never ends, like chasing a mirage where the finish line is always moving forward.

Ideals are presented as if meeting the goal is like arriving at a destination where the effort and work stop after you arrive. Once you reach that destination, you will be given your reward, which will be permanent, and you'll be released from the pressure to focus, perform, and dedicate yourself to proving yourself for the rest of your life. In reality, this is not how it works. In truth, the harder you work, the farther away the goal gets when striving for value through body image, not only because of increased needs for food, but because the bar rises.

As people get closer and closer to achieving an ideal, there is more and more criticism, especially within oneself. Like being evaluated under a shifting microscope, focusing in and magnifying any flaws or defects, the bar rises again as soon as it has been reached. The goal gets increasingly strict and perfectionistic, making the end goal almost unachievable, and the work to reach it can be obsessively inhumane.

Magnifying the details of the body naturally increases criticisms and expectations, and the original destination the individual set out to achieve gets further and further away.

Like an indentured servant, she becomes a slave to continue to work and sacrifice—chasing a goal that is never good enough.

As well, the original weight-loss plan gets less effective, making the need to deprive food unrealistically strict. Consequently, her focus on food and/or exercise can become obsessive. And like gasoline on a fire, any praise or attention adds even more pressure on people to do whatever it takes to achieve more, or to do whatever it takes to keep the pride for their improved body image.

Motivation that was lenient, realistic, and steady in the beginning can quickly change to an all-or-nothing approach. As the goal gets stricter and less realistic, minor mistakes get catastrophized. They get distorted into being worse than they really are, thus creating a sense of increased failure, even when the original goal was met. Many people who expect more than what is within reach—and eventually quit in their efforts—experience feelings of embarrassment, shame, and inadequacy as a consequence.

Eventually, people end up eating more and more with longer periods of time between diets, thinking the weight gain will eventually get fixed by the next anticipated diet. The thinner look you originally set out to achieve becomes increasingly distant. Consequently, there's a significantly larger impulsive need to eat in anticipation for a longer and more severe famine. As a person chases the goal of being thinner, even if it isn't as thin as she previously wanted, the trigger to secure access to food will be perpetual. This is like being stuck in a monkey trap.

> **The Monkey Trap:** Because of the perceived benefits, chasing the mirage of thinness with dieting is like being stuck in a monkey trap. This is a trap or cage that has a piece of fruit in it, and when a hungry monkey puts its hand through the hole and grabs the fruit, its newly filled fist becomes too large to exit the cage. He would have to release the fruit in order for his fist to be small enough to get out. If the monkey is not willing to let go of the fruit, he will remain trapped with the fruit in his hand that's stuck in the cage.

The illusion is that the fruit is attainable, and it is, but only to be held and only inside cage. The sustenance, pleasure, and nutrition of the fruit aren't actually available to eat. If the monkey gets entranced by the illusion that it is possible he could eat the fruit he is holding onto, he will devote time, energy, and discomfort on something that is actually impossible. Like chasing a mirage, as the monkey gets hungrier, it becomes more entranced or dependent on the fruit in his hand, keeping him dedicated to something that isn't and will never be edible.

What the monkey thinks is lifesaving is, in fact, life expending, and potentially life-threatening. When he becomes aware that it is impossible to eat it, despite wasting time, life, health, and freedom, he will surrender the mirage of sustenance, let go of the fruit, and set himself free.

Many people who suffer cycling between dieting and emotional eating want to be free from the misery, insanity, and limitation of the trap; however, they also want to keep the prize that continues to keep them in that cage.

In order to be set free from the misery of the trap cycling between dieting, bingeing, dieting, emotional eating and dieting again, the person must be willing to let go of the sustenance and benefit of dieting and emotional eating. Some people aren't willing to let go of their thin supremacy and want to keep the symbol of their worth attached to a body image that allows them to "fit in." Some people want the emotional protection she gets from bingeing, which means dieting is necessary in order to fix the physical damages.

**Whatever it is that a person gets out of it, she'd have
to give that up if she wants permanent freedom from
the darkness and misery of viciously cycling
between dieting and emotional eating.**

157

Like the monkey letting go of the fruit to gain freedom from the trap, she'd have to face surrendering what she perceives is important to her survival. She'd have to face her fears of not "fitting in" and accept the truth without any self-defense.

SECTION 5

When Shame Threatens Your Survival

A Client Wrote:

> "To me, Robin was like the angel standing in the middle of hell, showing me where the door to get out was. She educated me on Maslow's hierarchy of needs, narcissism, codependency and boundaries, where unhealthy ideas about food come from, and so many concepts. By the time I reached out for Robin's help, it wasn't hard for me to turn my life around because I really had nowhere else to turn."

> "For the first time, *I learned how to give myself grace*, and what compassion actually feels like. And I'll never forget when, in the ashes of my life, I first found that eternal smile that lives in the heart—this eternal presence of a creative force that lives inside of each of us. I imagine it's the place prisoners of war find when their spirit cannot be affected by the external treatment they are receiving. And I realized that I had compassion and grace I could give to others. I found my heart and what it means to live from it. And I divorced all concepts of dieting and restricting, and especially of *seeing myself as a failure.*"

In the past, I had tried every diet in the book, in an attempt to "control" myself. I hardly ever even think about food now because I am too busy living life. Through Robin's contributions to the world, I do believe my life was saved. It seems so radical compared to the diet industry's rhetoric, but I truly understand that the mental prison of the restrictions we place on ourselves is far, far worse than eating some food considered "forbidden." What came after what had felt like I was facing death was true life and freedom. I walked away from that mental prison, and I sincerely hope each and every person struggling finds his or her own way out. The fact that Robin didn't just free herself, but turned around to free as many other people as she can reach, is a testament to how beautiful and powerful her work is."

Chapter 13

"Fitting In" and Survival Mode

"Authenticity is the daily practice of letting go of who we think we're supposed to be and embracing who we are."
– Dr. Brené Brown, research professor and author

Restrictive eating while living surrounded by food in abundance can more often than not, trigger self-preserving survival mechanisms to fight for access to food—especially when the reasons a person is voluntarily restricting food are superficial. But why would a person do this? For some people, restrictions are set in place because of allergic reactions to certain types of food. For others, it's for a temporary spiritual fast, or a medical procedure. For most, however, dieting is done as an attempt to lose weight in order to reduce survival fears of not "fitting in," as well as reduce perceptions of not being worthy of acceptance, inclusion, or belonging.

> **NOTE:** As I've monitored thousands of rounds of Dr. Simeons' hCG protocol, I've found symptoms of psychological stress associated with starvation in most participants. However, the more a person's motivation to do the protocol is emotionally driven to improve his or her negative body image and self-worth, I observed significantly more intense feelings of victimhood and deprivation,

which resulted in impulsive desires to deviate from the protocol, emotionally eat, and binge eat after the process was over.

These participants weren't able to keep a neutral and open-minded perspective, and ended up negatively blowing out of proportion both the very low-calorie protocol as well as the weight-loss results. Also, as the motivation to follow the protocol was emotionally based on weight and size loss, the need to micromanage the physical results became obsessive.

For this reason, I believe it's imperative that anyone planning to do Dr. Simeons' hCG protocol understand the degree her motivation is based on thin-supremacy body-image beliefs. This understanding is important no matter what type of diet or food restriction a person is planning to reinforce. He or she needs to recognize how much their emotional eating stems from survival impulses for food. They need to grasp the drive to control food and lose weight that has nothing to do with their body, and everything to do with the survival need to "fit in."

Based on the research and findings of Dr. Abraham Maslow, the human need for being included is vitally important and was incorporated in his hierarchy of needs. However, it is third in priority behind environmental safety and physiological needs such as food and water.

Maslow's Third Hierarchy of Need: Love and Belonging

Maslow's third hierarchy of need encompasses the innate motivation to feel worthy of love and to be seen as a valuable member of one's community—and to have something to give, something to share, and something to add to the society. It also encompasses our instincts to avoid, deny, hide from, and prevent criticism, ridicule, embarrassment, guilt, and shame.

**Maslow's third hierarchy of need is very important
because when working functionally with others as a team
to survive, the primary, more-important hierarchies
of need are more likely to be fulfilled.**

Working with others improves access to vital needs for life, reducing the risk of death.

A person's perceptions of being important to a group increases confidence in his or her survivability—that there's security in advance of threat or danger. In addition, as roles and relationships in a group become more predictable and secure, the capacity to explore, mate, and to innovate expands. These benefits can make it seem as if the third hierarchy of need—to be included and belong—is more important than the first and second hierarchy of needs. However, as working with others brings increased capacity to survive, it also brings competition, shared resources, relationship and communication problems, and the risk for being judged and rejected. Perceptions of not being valued by others feels as if you're at higher risk for uncontrollable death.

MASLOW'S HIERARCHY OF NEEDS

SURVIVAL ALONE, COMPARED TO SURVIVAL WITH OTHERS: Imagine something cataclysmic happens and you have to survive in the wilderness, where alone you have to hunt and forage for food and water. You must find and create shelter, as well as find coverings/clothes to protect you from the elements. All of this must be done by you alone, in a way that sustains your life through all seasons. Your unconscious survival-oriented mind would shift your conscious experience to feel impelled with tunnel vision, which is to harness energy toward securing food, water, protection, and shelter before anything else.

If you were with one or two other people, this challenge wouldn't seem as dire, and the focus on the necessary work would slightly relax. If you were in a group of twenty to forty people, confidence in your survival would improve. The work to survive would distribute to each person, and the tunnel vision on food, shelter, and safety would widen and relax further. It wasn't that long ago that people survived independently in this type of small group.

You could say this need and motivation to belong is based on the fact that humans are similar to other pack animals, like dogs, that thrive when working together to support life. But this comes with the downside of being territorial, competitive, and with pecking orders when resources are insecure or scarce. No different from dogs that act out when neglected and abused, we too function and survive better when we feel secure, can give and receive love, and experience a sense of purpose. For this reason, a great deal of psychological wiring that drives motivation is geared to preserve and defend ourselves from judgment, rejection, and abandonment.

Abandonment and Rejection

Evolutionary psychologists theorize that our inherent drive to belong in a group stems from tens of thousands of years with dramatic improvements to survivability and safety that occurred when people lived in small groups, helping and working together as a team. Ultimately, this evolved into a survival need, to the point that our motivation to feel valued and safe with others feels like a life-or-death matter.

Our brains have been wired to release pleasurable signals of safety when we have a purpose in the group, are accepted, needed, and loved. However, our brains are also wired to experience withdrawal and negative irritating fight-or-flight signals when we perceive there is potential threats tied to being demoted or rejected. Those signals are more intense:

1) the more inadequate a person feels within him or herself, and
2) the more a person needs his or her group to survive.

According to evolutionary psychology, our inborn drive to avoid rejection evolved in times of disease and scarcity to prioritize survival of the group over the survival of the individual. If there was food shortage or famine, the group would prioritize rations of food for those that contributed and were perceived as beneficial to the group. The sick and needy were often stigmatized, given less food, and in dire situations, were abandoned to fend for themselves in the wilderness, which meant certain death. *Rejection, when survival is dependent on your tribe, equates to death.*

As an evolved danger, the perception of abandonment, or being worthy of abandonment, still triggers fight-or-flight mechanisms today, as if we still live in the wilderness and will die alone if we don't secure relationships with others.

If someone important to you is disappointed in you, you aren't going to die, but emotionally it can feel catastrophic. When there's apparent threat of disapproval, the brain has warning mechanisms that are like loud sirens, bright flashing lights, and magnified threat signals that get triggered when something dangerous seems to be happening. Immediately, involuntary self-preserving defense mechanisms get activated, which is similar to if you were encountering a dangerous predator. You feel the urge to fight, freeze in your tracks, or run away and hide.

In the case of social condemnation, your mistake and the group's disapproval are the predator. In effect, when a person is radically insecure within herself, the need to be secure with family, friends, or community can take over all other survival needs.

> **NOTE:** This has been suggested as the reason why someone suffering with anorexia would rather die of starvation than to gain weight. The way to survive in her mind relies more heavily on avoiding body fat than it does eating. I assume this type of survival, where being thin is more important than food, is a phenomenon that occurs in environments where food is abundant, and thinness is worshipped as a social virtue. If left to survive in a third-world environment where food is scarce, and where poverty and emaciation are the norm, would she still fear body fat and avoid eating when food is available?

Adapting to "Fit In" and the Mirage of Inclusion

When it comes to survival and the psychological wiring to seek inclusion in a tribe, the mind unconsciously gravitates to what is repetitive and seen positively as a clear and direct path to safety through "fitting in." This is what happens when you repeatedly see pictures of idealized body images through the media and in your community. Eventually the mind adapts to this repetition as a signal of safety, and there are feelings of pleasure when you speak, act, and dress like those around you.

In essence, when people seek to achieve a body image, they are often seeking to secure the urge to "fit in" which seems to diminish threats to their third hierarchy of need. If being different feels exposing, unsafe, and vulnerable to disapproval, it would make sense to create an alternative identity based around predictable concepts of acceptability. This is similar to animals that blend into their environment (camouflage) in order to not stick out. Humans are impelled to do the same thing, and *this isn't always a bad thing!*

It would be understandable that a person perceived as different or "unsafe" would want to change the way she looks, and try to imitate others so that she doesn't stand out, seem threatening, or draw negative attention to herself. Mechanisms that direct energy and focus toward securing one's safety, get harnessed toward memorizing, learning, and consuming as much informa-tion as possible to become what is predictably valued in society. The down-side of this type of harnessed focus is that it ensures a person will know far more about cultural ideals than she does her innate and truthful human qualities.

The consequence is not being able to tell the difference between subjective cultural fantasy about what and who a person should be from one's objective authentic self. You end up internalizing an identity that is actually a biased cultural concept, thinking it is your true self. *You believe you are and should be what is accepted.* The problem isn't the instinct to adapt, but rather believ-ing that if you don't conform, you are unworthy of love and inclusion.

Instead of staying true to one's original and authentic self, she misdirects her identity outward towards a seemingly innocent, less-rejectable role that is based around social inclusion. However, this outward goal keeps her perpetually chasing a mirage that she assumes when reached, will secure her third hierarchy of need.

When a person needs others to validate her value and worth to "fit in", her mind will be in perpetual survival mode as she attempts to reach a moving target—especially when the standards rise as they are reached. Unfortunately, a person who thinks this way about herself often projects those feelings out-ward toward others—believing that if they don't conform, they too are un-worthy of love and inclusion.

Ask Yourself:
- Have you been judged as not worthy of inclusion because of your shape and size?
- Have you judged yourself as not worthy of inclusion because of your shape and size?
- Have you judged others as not worthy of inclusion because of their size and shape?

In cultures that promote thin supremacy, where fatter bodies are labeled as inferior, inadequate, and are assumed worthless, it would be expected that believers who are larger and don't "fit in," would show emotional signs of activated survival mechanisms directly tied to a threatened third hierarchy of need. They would experience feelings of shame, and would be driven to behave in such a way that defends and protects them from dangers of abandonment and rejection.

Not only would they feel impelled to hide, but to also fix the body that is perceived to be the source of shame.

> **This is why many people are attracted to dieting and radical restrictions like the hCG protocol. This is especially true when advertisements and media used to sell weight-loss programs promote images that imply improved self-esteem, confidence, and social inclusion. They are not just selling fat loss, but they are selling fat loss as a way to remove shame.**

When Shame Threatens Your Life

Like stigma being a visible mark of disgrace and indignity, shame is an emotion that arises when you believe you are—at your core—a failure, disgrace, and are worthy of abandonment. You can imagine, as it relates to Maslow's third hierarchy of need, shame is an emotion that might trigger the urge

168

to defend and protect oneself from apparent rejection, abandonment, and ultimately death.

> **NOTE:** As stigma and shunning elicits a sense of danger that you are at risk of being seen as having no social value, and that you are worthy of disapproval and being deserted to survive alone—the internal emotion of shame triggers the impulse to fend for individual survival needs in order to sustain life independent of others.[21]

> People living with chronic shame often experience paranoia, delusions, and psychosis, and are often cruel to themselves and others.[22] The thought is that if you believe you are worthy of shame, others are worthy of being shamed too.

The beliefs that define you and others as "bad" and worthy of rejection might trigger survival instincts for you to shrink and hide from perceived dangers that are attached to being rejected. Hard-wired impulses urge you to avoid exposure if you think you're at risk of being judged. Therefore, you might pull away from or desert people and vulnerable situations, *in fear you'll be judged by others the way you judge yourself,* and the way you've been judged in the past. It would seem safer to isolate and protect yourself from your "badness" by avoiding others, and instead, to seek what gives you a sense of safety, security, and pleasure by yourself.

Because you believe the societal dogma that defined you as "bad," like thin supremacy, you end up being your own worst enemy. You shame, punish, and abandon yourself before anyone else can, thinking the only way you can earn the right to survive is if you beg, reason, and rationalize with yourself that you deserve something rewarding, like food.

You become your own judge and jury—persecutor and rescuer. These shame-based pleasure-seeking behaviors are often linked to addiction.

Shame-Based Pleasure-Seeking Survival

The idea is that when you don't feel safe with your own family, friends, and society, our instincts are to take care of our insecurities by becoming self-preserving and self-soothing. In effect, you're protecting your ability to survive alone. But if your own sense of survivability feels too weak and insecure, the value of things that bring pleasure that also aren't reliant on others becomes more and more important. Drugs, alcohol, medication, but especially food, have been seen as a way to self-soothe, or to preserve one's own sense of survivability.[23]

Shame, and the loss of social status, enhances the value of Maslow's first and second hierarchies of need. According to scientists, the value of food goes up significantly as more shame is experienced.[23]

Food and other pleasurable stimulus mediate a temporary artificial sense of safety, security, and ease when your beliefs trigger inner survival mechanisms that tell you to fear others and yourself. To cope with abandonment, these outside pleasurable behaviors and substances provide an inner sense of safety and validation, without the risk of rejection. However, the side effect can have permanent consequences, and can damage your body, mind, and important relationships in your life. In the case of binge eating and shame about one's body, the result is increased body fat, increased shame, and increased urges to binge.

Weight Stigma and Emotional Eating

As people internalize images of thinness that symbolize acceptance, lovability, and inclusion without fear of rejection…it's no wonder they are driven to perpetually diet. However, as more and more people suffer from mental health problems resembling eating disorders, the social impact of stricter body images, stigma, and resulting extreme diets needs to be addressed—especially the impact that stigma has on the emotional-eating behaviors.

- **In a survey of 2,500 women, when asked how they cope with stigma about their weight, 79 percent reported that they turn to food as a coping mechanism, and that eating is a common way they deal with loneliness and stress.**[6]

- Another study done with over 1,000 women from a non-profit weight-loss support group found that women who believed the negative characterizations of weight stigma—*and blamed themselves*—binge ate more frequently, and experienced higher depression and anxiety. [20, 24]

- Compared to people who don't consider themselves over-weight, when exposed to a weight-stigmatizing stimulus, such as fitness magazines or other media, those who perceived themselves negatively as overweight ate more immediately after looking at the media. Regardless of the truth of their weight, if they believed they were overweight, they responded negatively to stigma exposure.[25, 26]

- In cultures of "thin supremacy," because the stigma and negativity attached to obesity is generally accepted, people who have more fat are more likely to experience social rejection, viewed as less desirable dating partners, have fewer friends, and spend less time with friends. This makes a person vulnerable to isolating herself, depression, anxiety, low self-esteem, poor body image, and in many cases, suicide.[24]

- Adults with obesity issues reporting weight stigmatization were three times more likely to have a binge-eating disorder diagnosis compared to people who haven't experienced weight stigma.[27]

- How a person relates to food is directly influenced by the degree that a person blames herself and believes the body-fat stigma coming from important people in her life. The more stigma a person experiences, *and the more she believes it within herself*, the more likely she is to develop a binge-eating disorder.[28]

- Among adults with more body fat, when they experience greater weight bias in weight-loss treatment, they are more likely to eat more, lose less weight, refuse that their weight be monitored, and expend less energy through physical activity.[29]
- As people are in a vulnerable position to discuss their body, and are looking to medical professionals for help—being treated as if they are inferior, and aren't worthy of care, can be particularly detrimental. It compounds the sense of hopelessness, judgment, and prejudice they already experience socially.

Besides the increased likelihood of bingeing, in my opinion some of the most relevant research regarding shame and the body is about how internalized and experienced stigma relative to being overweight, influences the body's physiological "fight" response. The psychological stress experienced in regard to how weight is perceived negatively by others, has consistently shown to increase the physiological stress response that Dr. Cannon described as "fight-or-flight," discussed in chapter 10. In other words, *shame about your weight puts your mind and body in a state of survival mode.*

"Fight or Flight" and Shame

A growing body of research is beginning to question the mind-and-body paradigm, especially the science and research that indicates weight stigma as a significant factor promoting psychological coping mechanisms. This encourages isolation, overeating, and reduced physical activity, but also a biological sensitivity to weight gain.

A person who believes in thin supremacy will respond to judgment and shame about body fat as if it's a life-threatening enemy or an angry wild animal chasing her down, stimulating the fight-or-flight response. If she thinks she's overweight, she will live in fear, anxiety, and survival mode because of how dangerous her body is perceived, and this danger projects onto food—as if food is also threatening her survival.

According to the fight, freeze, or flight physiology described in chapter 10, these people would predictably have suppressed digestion, higher resting blood sugar levels, and increased activation of adrenalin and the fight response. Research has demonstrated such stress in people who have negative body image.

Studies show that stress associated with stigma and shame regarding one's weight increases stress induced C-reactive protein levels (inflammatory marker associated to heart disease), blood pressure, cortisol levels, and oxidative stress.[30] Among other things, this response increases the susceptibility to fat gain, even when food isn't eaten to excess.

As well, media exposure to weight stigma, *for people who believe it about themselves,* showed a significant increase in cortisol production. People who don't believe these things, don't have the same response when they are exposed to weight stigma.[31, 32]

This means that a person who is ashamed of her weight and believes she is "bad" because of it, experiences signals of danger when she sees derogatory media about overweight people.

Imagine the effect that this type of stress a person experiences daily has on a person's mind and body over a long period of time, from childhood into adulthood. This alone would make anybody susceptible to hair loss, thyroid ailments, autoimmune disorders, heart attacks, diabetes, weight gain, etc.— *even if she isn't overeating.* This is especially true when you add the fact that people who experience stigma avoid the embarrassment of being made fun of by isolating themselves.

NOTE: This embarrassment and fear of being made fun of has shown reduced motivation to exercise in both children and adults,

173

ultimately promoting elevated blood pressure and increased physiological stress.[18, 33]

Research correlating the stigma of obesity and internalization of that shame over the course of the last decade—*to the susceptibility of weight gain, stress, anxiety, isolation, reduced motivation to exercise, depression, stress eating, binge eating, psychological and physiological stress factors*—is overwhelming strong.

Combine that with the psychological response showing a significant increase in binge-eating behavior—no matter what starting weight, age, BMI, race/ethnicity, or socioeconomic factor—for anyone who experiences and internalizes weight stigma, they are going to end up with obesity.[34, 35, 30]

In other words, for those who believe it, weight stigma increases their personal likelihood of becoming and remaining obese. *The belief in the stigma of obesity alone increases your risks.*

In terms of helping the "epidemic of obesity," it would be better to call it an "epidemic of fat stigma," coming from a cultural epidemic of thin supremacy.

When Your Body Threatens Food and Food Threatens Your Body

When the body experiences perceived danger or threat, it is beneficial and lifesaving to have the resulting survival response. But if what triggers threat is shame associated with the conditions of the body, wouldn't that mean the survival response would be triggered by the "badness" of the body? In addition, when the solution is to restrict food, perceived danger is also triggered by an important life-sustaining necessity: food. Unfortunately, people who believe in thin supremacy live in complete fear and anxiety about their body and food. This seems ridiculous when you consider that the body is responsible for sustaining life, and so is food.

It makes sense that so many people live with poor body image when the only body that seems to be safe from discrimination and judgment is a thinner body. They dedicate their life to enforcing food restrictions in order to be thinner—but end up living in constant tension about seeking access to food. When that thinner body requires permanent food restriction, it's as if the only way to be seen as lovable is if you're willing to starve yourself. And when people eventually break down and feed the impulses driving them to eat, they are deemed failures without questioning the influence that diets have on triggering primal urges to eat. In my opinion, this is cruel and inhumane.

I cannot tell you how many people I've met and discussed these issues with who have dedicated most of their adult life, and some of their childhood, to feeling bad about their body and their weight.

It's understandable why multiple generations feared body fat, and thus put their children on diets to help them "battle their weight." They thought they were protecting the future from the judgment, shame, and abandonment that theyand others experienced for being unhealthy, diseased, and "overweight."

They were battling for the need to "fit in" and to be worthy of love and belonging. However, they didn't know that feeling bad about body fat, being ashamed of your body, and perpetual dieting promotes overeating—and the aftereffect is even more weight gain.

If you want to make a positive impact towards reducing the incidence of emotional eating and eating disorders, it would be better to be inclusive, loving, understanding, and open to people whose weight and size is larger. To recognize that the more shame a person attaches to her body fat, the more likely she is to diet, emotionally eat, binge, stay at home, and continue to gain more weight.

Ask Yourself:

- ☐ Have you experienced shame, judgment, and rejection because of your body?
- ☐ How did that impact your personal sense of value?
- ☐ Have you experienced social anxiety and distress because of fears about your body?
- ☐ Were you more accepted and liked because of the way your body looked?
- ☐ If body image was removed from the way you define your worth, how would that impact your life?

Is Weight Loss Healthy If:

- ☐ It's motivated by an image of being accepted by others?
- ☐ It requires a person to obsess over her body, over food, and over exercise?
- ☐ She has a fear response around food, and has to micromanage everything she eats?
- ☐ The food restrictions require she isolates herself from social eating and celebrations?
- ☐ Stress about one's weight stimulates the survival response from the brain that stimulates cortisol and other metabolic reactions that promote fat gain, even when eating is less?

"Diets are essentially training courses in how to feel fat and feel like a failure."
– Paul McKenna, Life Coach and Author

Chapter 14

When Being Thinner isn't an Option

"The Method holds participants accountable for a source of motivation that is not limited by a fleeting resolve for weight reduction. It exposes dysfunctional eating and other compensations for insecurity, giving merit to authentic and genuine emotional strength. This process gives you an opportunity to break away from the codependency cycle between dieting and emotional eating, and freedom from the emotional limitations of both. The result is emotional strength and a body set free from the torments of abuse."
– *Weight-Loss Apocalypse*, chapter 11 page 126

Time Wasted and Freedom Lost

Imagine living this way for twenty, thirty, or even forty years of your life, being defined by your inability to lose body fat and sustain starvation long enough to achieve anything. In order to earn acceptance into a culture—one that encourages totalitarian concepts of thinness that requires starvation—it wouldn't be surprising when there's a tendency of disordered eating in those that dogmatically believe it.

This devotion and dedication of life to striving for goals that are inherently unrealistic, eliminates freedom to have other hopes and dreams that might actually be more emotionally and psychologically fulfilling. In essence, people are encouraged to chase unreachable standards in order to prove they are worthy of love and belonging, and they think by doing this they'll have confidence to live life in freedom the way that they want to.

The truth is, making unreachable standards the "gatekeeper" to acceptance, love, and belonging is a trap that wastes large amounts of energy and time, and loses freedom in life.

Many of the people I've worked with in their fifties, sixties, and seventies grieve the life they didn't live because they were too infatuated and distracted by the idea they had to be thinner before they could do what they really wanted. And to make matters worse, despite the amount of money, effort, and life they've devoted to their "battle with weight," they grieve the fact that their body is far bigger than it was originally before they had decided they needed to be thinner. But once you start the pendulum swinging between enforced food restrictions and consequential impulsive food consumption, it's very difficult to stop the cycle—especially when embarrassment and shame increases as you gain even more weight.

The worse a person feels about herself because of this struggle, the more rigid she'll approach diets. The stricter she diets, the more fragile she is to likely fail, and the more intense grows her desire to eat. Eventually, this cycle ends in more and more weight gain. Any person who lives this way is set up from the get-go to perpetually chase the conditions that are sold as "easy" ways to fulfill her desire to feel lovable, included, and to belong. And even if she does reach the body image, the freedom doesn't exist due to the continued effort, energy, and devotion necessary to maintain ideals that aren't naturally sustainable.

If it took a form of starvation to be thinner, typically it will take continued starvation to sustain being thinner. Ultimately, even when the fantasy body image is reached, and security in a thin-supremist culture is earned, the attack to one's access to food will have to continue, and survival impulses to eat will remain. Eventually, food will need to be eaten to stay alive, and weight will be regained. The cycle between dieting, weight loss, emotional eating, and weight gain goes around and around and around. The only way for this cycle to stop is to die or to surrender any dieting and ultimately to surrender the ideal body image.

To do this you'd have to secure your sense of worth, lovability, and belonging without body image, and your need to fit in. You'd have to secure the third hierarchy of need that directly threatens your first, and more important hierarchy of need.

Independence: Can You Take Care of Yourself?

Maslow's third hierarchy of need *to feel lovable and belong* is far more complicated and complex than the first and second more important needs that are required for life. The third hierarchy of need isn't essential to stay alive like food is, but it has evolved as a need that is vital and has great impact on our emotional wellbeing. Access to food and shelter is straightforward, whereas relationships with others is vulnerable to 1) your ability to take care of yourself, 2) how you feel about yourself, and 3) how others feel about you.

Securing this hierarchy of need relies heavily on our own perception of personal worth, as well as our sense of capacity to survive if we are left on our own. If you could independently adapt to challenge and find a way to provide your own needs, chances are you'd be less impacted by negative criticism than someone who is highly dependent on others to survive. And when you experience judgment and criticism, with a personal sense of worth, you're less likely to be triggered into self-defense, or take it personally.

A sense of personal capacity to adapt and learn skills necessary to take care of oneself is described as *competence.* Competence is what drives the energy and aptitude necessary to teach oneself, or to figure out how to make it on your own. Without competence, a person's need for assistance goes up. If that help comes from other people, your need to "fit in" and receive validation would increase.

When dependent on others, feeling unwanted,
unneeded, unappreciated, without value, lonely,
or without something to give, would justifiably
elicit emotional triggers of life-or-death stress.

Without personally securing one's "self" first, symptoms of survival mode, such as anxiety, competition, paranoia, perfectionism, and the pressure to perform, would drive much of the mental state and work of an individual. Although, as these survival emotions might increase productivity and willingness to conform, it also might increase emotional tension between one's mind and other members of her community.

In order to fulfill Maslow's *third hierarchy of need to belong,* it's not a matter of getting rid of the primitive sensitivity to being rejected and abandoned, but rather bypassing it with self-competence and grace to be real with oneself and others. This is true even when it's inevitable that others might not like or approve of you *if you don't conform to their needs.* At the same time, it is important to be able to adapt and adjust to your environment in a way that is least detrimental to yourself and others.

This complex hierarchy of need is satisfied by two simple solutions:

1.) To develop competence in one's ability to independently adapt and provide for him or herself, and
2.) To perceive from within that he/she is integrally lovable and deserving of love, even if she/he makes mistakes, isn't the

best, or might actually be the weakest, dumbest, ugliest, or worst person for the job.

In order to securely fulfill the third hierarchy of need, without it being vulnerable to outside opinion, you'd need to determine, *for yourself*, that you are worthy of love and belonging, even if others, including loved ones, don't agree—and even if you don't meet the ideal standards or "fit in." Only you have access to the integrity of the life you feel on the inside. I call this "life space."

This is the space of life that you are experiencing and only you are aware of. If you aren't willing to face this "life space" and recognize its worth, how can you expect someone else to do it for you, especially if you aren't willing to express it? How can others have a sense of who you truthfully are if you don't value it or use it?

> **You'd have to be willing to express the integrity you feel**
> **inside in order for them to recognize it. In other words,**
> ***it is impossible for others to approve of you and your life***
> ***if you don't approve of you or your life first.***

In order to fulfill this survival need, you alone are responsible to determine if you are intrinsically worthy of love and inclusion, even if you are extrinsically flawed and inadequate.

Ask Yourself:
- [ ] What's wrong with being innocently flawed?
- [ ] Why is being inferior such a bad thing?
- [ ] If you are *in truth* inadequate, not as good, or not the best, are these things worthy of shame?

For someone who has developed a sense of competence, as well as fulfilled your sense of worth by accepting your natural and inherent truths, positive or negative opinions don't make or break the security needed to fulfill the third hierarchy of need to belong—especially if you aren't afraid of your truth of being viewed as inferior. In that case, *no one's opinion really matters.*

Giving Up Being Thinner

For most people, it isn't until they reach complete and total exhaustion, fatigue, and misery with the process of dieting and bingeing, and re-dieting and bingeing, that they are willing to face the reality that maybe they should give up dieting and accept their body in order to start living again—even when it will be criticized and judged. In essence, they are willing to accept failure, forgive themselves, and move on. But when your body has gained a significant amount of size and weight, this process is very difficult.

For a person who has gained more body fat than she ever thought she'd allow, it seems as if dieting is the only way to 1) rescue her from feeling out of control with food, 2) remove the weight she's already gained, and 3) protect her from gaining even more weight. However, if she took a step back to look at how dieting has enabled her dysfunctional relationship with food, she'd see that dieting has been a primary source of strain, anxiety, and shame about eating that underlies the emotional charge behind the drive to over-consume. The hardest part of recovery for most people is accepting that to stop bingeing she'll need to stop dieting, which means she'll have to accept her fears and assumptions that without a diet she'll:

- Never lose weight again.
- Have to accept her current weight and size, and every aspect of it that she doesn't like.
- Gain weight and could get even bigger.
- Regain the weight lost after the most recent diet.

She'll have to accept her rubbing thighs, her aching knees from extra pounds, and the fear that she might die of every issue/threat that the weight-loss industry uses in order to scare their followers. According to the weight-loss industry, it is presumed you'll be unhealthy, die early, will never get married, won't have children, your loved ones will abandon you, and you'll be alone forever.

> **The fear thoughts are innumerable, and those fear thoughts bring about even more fear thoughts, all of which seem like a tsunami wave of death you can't handle.**

And to make matters more difficult in a culture that shames and stigmatizes body fat, accepting your weight and size when you're considered "too big" or not thin enough would be like allowing others to judge you and dismiss you as an inferior, insignificant, and lesser human being.

When it seems that losing body fat is the only way you'll feel good about your life and be confident in yourself, not going on a diet to rescue yourself would go against strong survival instincts demanding you do something to protect yourself from being judged and discarded like a piece of trash. These fears come across as truthful and realistic, and when there's an easy way to fix, escape, and repress them, it doesn't make sense to accept them without self-defense.

Signals of danger awaken primitive fears of being alone, as if you'll never experience happiness and joy again, or that without a diet your life might as well be over. For many people, letting go of disordered-eating behaviors feels as if your life will be irreparably damaged or permanently disfigured—even though the dieting and resultant emotional eating and bingeing destroy both your body and the freedom of your life.

When Being a Martyr Keeps the Misery Going

It's easy to feel sorry for yourself for having to let go of these behaviors, even though life with them is full of shame, fear, horror, darkness, isolation, and disconnection from life. You feel like a powerless victim scratching at the surface to get away. Having a "poor-me" pity party, as if you're a martyr for having to recover from the miserable cycle of shame, dieting, emotional eating, and shame again, is a last-ditch effort to stay attached to chasing the mirage of being thinner and worthy of love, even though it's incredibly abusive and harmful to your life.

Part of the problem is that it seems as if the fear, negative judgments, and feelings of victimhood and ruin will be *permanent,* and as if the feelings of emptiness and loss will be unrelenting for the rest of your life. Whereas dieting provides some sense of hope or possibility for happiness—despite the fact it is only a fantasy or mirage. It seems as if you have only two choices: 1) vulnerability, fear, and assumed pain or 2) a hopeful fantasy of weight loss with the predictable misery of dieting.

On one hand, you could endure a tortured existence, abusing yourself so you don't have to face your fears or the fact that you don't think you can handle them. Or on the other hand, you could refuse to respond to that fear, and face excruciating terror and loss that feels like it will kill you. For this reason, it feels as if the abusive behavior that exists between dieting and emotional eating are inescapable.

Most people feel safer in their dysfunctional relationship with food than they do the vulnerability of freedom, even though it ruins their health, body, relationships, and life. Before you know it, 1) you're either binge eating as a feast before the next famine, 2) obsessing over your next diet, 3) exercising in the middle of the night, or 4) seeking a bathroom or trashcan you can puke food into. However, being a slave to these behaviors eventually becomes hopelessly miserable and is without reward, *and the only way to recover is to give it up.*

There is freedom and peace in facing the vulnerable truth to humbly admit complete and total failure, without blame, self-defense, or excuse. It means you are liberated from having to fight to prove otherwise, and free from having to defend yourself from threat.

What Happens When Being Thinner Isn't an Option?

When I have clients visualize what life would be like if they had to live with a limitation, like losing the ability to walk or becoming blind, I have them ponder what would happen to the grievance they now hold about their body fat.

More often than not, clients find it easier to grieve, accept, and adapt to permanent physical disability in their mind than they do to forever stay overweight, or obese. To them, having a physical disability isn't a choice that can be remedied. However, having more body fat can be fixed.

When having the option of changing a fatter body to a thinner body, a person doesn't have to accept her weight or surrender her ideal body image, and can keep her position to be negative about her body. I have found that catastrophizing, magnifying, or turning up the negative volume towards body fat increases when people have the option of changing their weight. For this reason, clients have a hard time accepting *they will never lose weight again.*

However, if they can wrap their mind around making being thinner not an option, like losing a body part, they did foresee a grieving process, similar to what it would take to accept the death of a loved one, or a permanent physical limitation like losing their legs. Their position would change from denial, to anger, feeling sorry for themselves, feeling worthless, then to sadness, and finally to acceptance.

One way I help people feel this freedom is to intentionally visualize what would happen to their grievance with their body if they became permanently blind. Surprisingly, many of those people find the idea of being blind relieving, freeing, and liberating, as if losing their eyesight gives freedom from having to care or worry about their weight.

Not only does being blind make the negativity about body weight trivial by comparison, but it makes criticism about the way a person looks irrelevant. Being blind gives people freedom from being defined by looks to "fit in" as well as internalized body images. They get a feeling of what it would be like to connect to their surroundings with their other senses, and it gives them relief from being so intensely self-centered about the way they look.

If they can black out or go "blind" to body image, they can experience freedom from being defined by how their body is positively or negatively perceived visually. This gives them a sense of how they'd relate to their body if they could accept it exactly how it is, as if they are blind to "thin supremacy."

From this acceptance I noticed the intensity or volume of people's dissatisfaction made a dramatic change. They'd calm down and recognize that, in the grand scheme of life, their body *was actually pretty good.* Their issues weren't as bad or catastrophic as they made them out to be, and the body they currently live in is manageable, and worthy of gratitude. Often people would respond with intense relief, as if having to be the same weight would allow them to move on and free their life from the pressure and misery of having to devote their life energy to dieting and fixing their body. This is the freedom they thought they'd get after losing weight.

Our goal is to help them realize freedom doesn't exist with being thinner, but with accepting their body.

This made me question and look at how the perceived changeability of the body, in relation to idealized body images, serves as a potential factor that increased, and even promoted the intensity of distortion and dissatisfaction people had with their body. Giving people flexibility to change their body automatically promoted a socially more accepted body image that's better than what they have—increasing discontent, agitation, and for some, disgust with their current body. Having to face the loss of what they wanted, and to face acceptance instead, isn't easy, especially when they have the option of continuing to pursue the social benefits they think weight loss would give them.

To let go of idealized body images of thinness would require that a person accept the loss of what she wanted and what would benefit her by losing body fat. Freedom gained from relinquishing a "superior" body image comes at a price. Like a contract, the costs must be consciously agreed upon. Even if the feared costs aren't guaranteed, they must be entirely accepted in order to relieve oneself from caring about and defending herself from the slightest possibility.

Examples are:
- ✓ If a person attached being thinner to the opportunity to find a mate and get married, giving up being thinner would feel like she's giving up partnership and marriage, and that could potentially mean giving up having children too. It's not that she has to remove her desire to get married, but that she isn't willing to sacrifice mind and body for someone else's gratification.
- ✓ If being thinner provides parental approval, proof that she isn't a failure, or safety from feeling judged, then she has to accept parental disapproval, being thought of as a failure, and judgment. The key here is eliminating body images from being defining factors in how she personally identifies her worth, even if important people in her life believe otherwise.
- ✓ If being thinner gives her a sense of safety and permission to eat emotionally, to accept her body would mean she'd have to accept the physical ailments and limitations that are a consequence of overeating as a coping mechanism.

A person must develop enough self-worth and respect for her life to recognize the cost of gaining other's approval, even through narcissistic concepts of body image, are too high. Nobody should have to live in continuous misery because of dieting, in isolation from food, and obsessed about her weight and size in order to provide someone else the momentary pleasure of thinking she's "good enough."

The goal is that she becomes indifferent to other's approval or disapproval in order to free her focus and direction in life to be self-determined.

For many people who believe in "thin supremacy," accepting their body as it is with the fat it has, feels not only cruel but impossible.

They think the only way to feel good and comfortable with their body is if it's thinner. They put their entire life on pause to instead focus, devote energy and mind power to dieting, monitoring food, and measuring their size and weight. Without the option of being thinner, they believe their life will be doomed forever.

They think they wouldn't go out in public; they wouldn't attend parties, travel, or go to the beach ever again. People assume if they had to be overweight the rest of their life, that their life would be worthless—*that they are worthless.* However, when they can no longer tolerate a life of misery with suffering from continuous anxiety about dieting, obsessiveness and fear about food, bingeing, starving, and hiding because of the shame attached to their weight, the only thing a person can do is look at diminishing her need to be thinner.

Letting go of thin-supremacy body images have the benefit of never having shame while eating, which is inherent to judgmental dieting.

You no longer have to fear about having one bite too much, eating at the wrong time, or eating something on the "bad" list of foods. What you eat will no longer make or break how you define your day.

I often ask new clients how it would feel, and what would happen if they were relieved forever from having to lose weight. What would it feel like to erase "be thinner" and dieting from their list of things to do, forever?

Acceptance removes the perceptual distortions attached to the conditions of their body and, for many people, brings about a calm, peaceful freedom, especially when they realize by permanently accepting their body as it is, they end their "battle with weight." It is then that people understand they would, in fact, go to the beach, travel, and go to parties. They wouldn't have to put their life on pause for anything anymore. For some people, they've put their life on hold battling weight for most of their entire life. Losing weight and dieting became their purpose in life, and experiencing a sense of freedom from it feels intensely liberating, and for some, like a rebirth to a new life.

It is at this point that people can see that having to lose weight or be thinner isn't a necessary condition in order for them to be happy, to be loved, or to feel good about themselves. They realize the problem isn't their body, but rather the attached freedom and happiness to the ideal body image internalized in their head. *They comprehend it's time for them to leave the cult of thin supremacy.*

When is Dr. Simeons' HCG Protocol Appropriate?

I believe Dr. Simeons' hCG protocol is appropriate only for people who are no longer emotionally triggered into survival mode because of fears of "health" or opinions about her body and weight. This would mean—no matter what size, shape, and health problems she has because of chronic fear, shame, and hiding with diet and binge-eating impulses—that she forgives herself, her body, and the belief systems that underlie the shame about her body. She would have to give the concept of thin supremacy and "health" grace, so that she no longer holds herself and others to it as if it's a survival need.

In doing so, opinions about her body and about her worthiness of love and inclusion lose power and becomes irrelevant and non-threatening.

Giving the body-image beliefs grace means they are given lenience, and to do this those beliefs must be questioned. The concept of thin supremacy must be looked at and recognized, not as a superior belief to be aspired to, but rather as a cruel ideology that leads to a life of psychological misery and physical pain, especially when it requires chronic food restriction. Body images that were internalized need to be externalized, so that a person's mind and body can get relief from the cognitive distortions and pressures of survival mechanisms. So they can become open-minded to the body.

They'd have to leave the cult of thin supremacy in order to accept their body unconditionally. Once this process is fully and completely done, then a person would be considered as a candidate for Dr. Simeons' hCG protocol, and only if their body meets appropriate criteria. With guidance, only then would a person be able to experience the psychological strain of the very low-calorie protocol with less risk of being triggered into feelings of fear, deprivation, and rebound urges to cycle between dieting and bingeing again.

Chapter 15

Leaving the Cult of Thin Supremacy

"A surrendered person can eat anything or go anywhere and is no longer subject to fears of contaminants, pollutants, drafts, germs, electromagnetic frequencies or food dyes. Our perception of the body shifts... This shift of perception is from 'I am the body' to 'I have a body.'"
– Dr. David R. Hawkins, *Letting Go: The Pathway of Surrender*, page 242

Turning People Away from the HCG Protocol

Emails and requests to work with me come in cycles, with some predictability to it. I usually get contacted to help people prepare for the hCG protocol some time in November and December. These are people who plan to start the very low-calorie protocol in January. Predictably, starting in February and throughout March I get contacted by people seeking help with emotional eating and binge eating. They reach out for my help about a month or two after reinforcing a restrictive diet as a New Year's resolution. They feel miserable, dejected, out of control, and ashamed that they've failed their resolution and regained lost weight. The other time this cycle occurs is with dieting that starts up again in the spring and predictably ends in emotional and binge eating during the summer months.

For other people, there is no predictable cycle because dieting and emotional eating is occurring every day, every week, all the time. Those clients typically reach out when they are in a dark space that feels like hell. They find me when searching for information on YouTube about eating disorders. They somehow find my YouTube channel in a sea of available content, like finding a needle in a haystack.

When someone finds my YouTube videos, takes the time to sift through and watch them, and then reaches out for my help, *they are already miserable.*

They've lived in psychological hell for so long that they are willing to listen to hour-long video discussions that bring up high levels of cognitive dissonance, or painful truths they don't want to hear. By the time they request my help, they've been through a cycle of thinking that what I suggest to clients in the videos is terrible, then questioning themselves—if what I'm saying might actually be true; then opening their mind to hear it without denial, rejecting it again; and then realizing more deeply the truth in what I'm suggesting. In order for them to end the misery, they will have to give up all forms of dieting, weight-loss methods, and the endeavor to be thinner.

The only way to heal is to accept you won't lose the weight you just gained, because you aren't going to diet...*for the rest of your life.* And with that, you'll have to accept permanent weight gain if you continue to binge and eat emotionally. This message can seem very confusing to people seeking guidance for Dr. Simeons' hCG protocol who find my YouTube channel.

On one hand, I'm encouraging people to abandon and become permanently abstinent to all forms of dieting, but on the other hand, I'm a huge fan of the hCG protocol. How could this be?

If I were to deny the benefits of losing fat when a person has hundreds of extra pounds of body fat to lose, pounds that contribute to significant limitations and physical distress, I would be ignorant. However, in my opinion, to suggest a person lose body fat without addressing how and why it was gained is far worse.

Of course, there is chronic strain that the body handles with:
- Physiological stress stemming from fear of rejection and abandonment.
- Perceived danger through the "badness" of the body and food.
- Physiological and nutritional deficits due to abrupt and prolonged food restriction.
- Survival mechanisms impelling the mind to gain access to food.
- Defense mechanisms agitating the mind to fight for food that's being deprived.
- Shame associated with failing to restrict food and being "out of control."
- The physical strain and stress from excessive food consumption.
- Shame and isolation as the body gains more body fat.
- Physical strain and stress from excessive food consumption before the next abrupt and prolonged food restriction.
- Bouts of extreme exercise, or extreme sedentary behaviors.
- This cycle, over and over again, for years, decade after decade.

Using the hCG protocol as a part of this cycle would be both psychologically and physically dangerous. To suggest the protocol as a means to heal hormonal imbalances linked to excess body fat without first addressing and stopping this vicious shame cycle would be like throwing gasoline on a raging fire. You'd be adding to and making the problem worse. Especially if a person successfully heals the body and loses a significant amount of weight, but then experiences more severe and catastrophic shame when they revert back to the diet-binge-diet cycle as they regain body fat that they took pride in losing.

For this reason, as people reach out for my help with the protocol, I discourage most people from it and suggest they eliminate it as an option.

**Until the desire for body images that might
be triggering insecurity and danger to your third
hierarchy of need are addressed and resolved,
I don't recommend any dieting or
food restrictions whatsoever.**

When I get a call from someone who is already on the very low-calorie protocol, the best advice I can give her is to stop monitoring her weight, and to prepare emotionally for when and if she regains the weight she's lost. My goal is to help her accept her fear of weight gain in order to discourage her from dieting once the protocol is over. The goal is to open her mind to the truth of her body, if she were to eat based on the biological rhythms of hunger. Even with my best effort, most people aren't willing to accept the truth of their body. They aren't willing to face letting go of the idea of thin supremacy.

**Until triggers for survival stemming from food
deprivation and thin-supremacy body images are gone,
the hCG protocol might pose risks of more harm
for a person's mind and body.**

However, when a person frees herself from the weight-loss dogma, accepts her body unconditionally, faces and accepts others' ignorant disapproval, and she lives in freedom from impulsive dieting and urges to eat emotionally for a long enough period of time, she might be a good candidate for the hCG protocol. This is true only if her body also meets appropriate criteria.

Even if a person has accepted her larger body unconditionally and is living free from the cycle of dieting and emotional eating, if her body reduces in size and weight, she will need to accept her thinner body unconditionally too if she wants to keep her freedom from the cycle of dieting and emotionally eating. *This means she'll need to accept the potential for weight regain after weight is lost,* otherwise she'll lose the freedom of her mind to instead focus on defending and preserving her thinner body. Her energy will be harnessed toward controlling food instead of living her life.

In order to hedge that risk, there is a process I take people through prior to considering the protocol as an appropriate form of physical rehabilitation or hormonal therapy. I call this part of the process the Mind of the Mind:Body Method. But prior to this, people must be willing to give up all forms and methods intended to prevent weight gain or to encourage weight loss.

Giving Up Diets and Weight-Loss Methods

When most people reach out for help, they aren't in the controlled weight-loss state of their misery. They don't ask for help until they are eating emotionally, bingeing, or "out of control." To help stop the "feasting before famine," a person must first remove the impending "famine." For some people, this is removing the idea that they're going to start the hCG protocol. For others it's removing the idea they are going to remove sugar from their diet tomorrow, or get back to carb free, or that they are going to do intermittent fasting. *To address the emotional aspects of body image, the food restrictions must be surrendered.*

Dieting is the reason why a person's first hierarchy of need is threatened while living in and surrounded by food that is in abundance.

Like a bear preparing for hibernation, her state of mind gets stuck on the "pre-famine setting" where she's supposed to eat in anticipation of being deprived for extended periods of time. It's a primitive mindset that clearly doesn't make sense in a world saturated with food with no actual famine in sight.

When a person commits to reinforcing an artificial famine, excessive eating ahead of time makes complete sense.

In a culture that worships and idolizes thinness, the constant reinforcement and pressure to diet is likely why the feasting mindset is triggered, no matter what her weight. In that case, it would be expected that a person would experience activated primitive defense mechanisms urging her to impulsively overeat while food is available, before and after she diets—even more so when the stress of dieting intensifies as her body gets bigger and bigger.

I ask clients who regularly binge: *"If it was impossible to lose the body fat that is gained after bingeing, would you still binge?"* Over the past 10 years in all of my discussions with people suffering with eating disorders, not one person has said, "Yes, I would binge anyway."

For people who binge and emotionally eat, dieting is the most powerful enabler and reason behind rationalizing, bargaining, and justifying excessive food consumption when there is no physical need. *Most overeaters don't consciously know this because they've always assumed and were told that food is the problem.*

Without a diet there wouldn't be:

- *Feelings of failure, shame, and guilt attached to bending the diet rules.*
  Not only do diets teach the concepts of "good" and "bad" food that promotes all-or-nothing thinking when it comes to food restrictions, but diets supply the black-or-white rules which require negotiations in order for people to believe they deserve and have earned the right to indulge. Without guilt for wanting to break the rules of a diet, a person wouldn't need to use emotions as a way to bargain for her right and entitlement for food. Emotional eating is, in

196

effect, eating that's been negotiated for with the rules of a diet's restrictions.

• *The need to argue for, and rationalize with emotional reasoning, the freedom to eat.*
Having to negotiate for food strengthens emotional bonds with food that have nothing to do with hunger or physical need. Food is eaten to celebrate, entertain, pacify, hide, avoid, distract, defend, repress, deny, decompress, retaliate, resent, punish, sooth, calm, procrastinate, etc. Some of these reasons for eating are normal and shouldn't be alarming. But if a person has to justify and negotiate with her dieting rules in order to repress guilt for wanting to eat, the amount of food she'll end up eating will be as large as the degree she negotiates.

Having to reason for food as if it's "forbidden fruit," inflates its importance.

• *A way to fix the consequential fat gain that results when food is eaten excessively for emotional reasons.*
I believe that emotional eating arises because dieting is used to fix the physical consequences, as if it's a "rescuer" and prevents people from having to take responsibility in the moment, and for the long-term aftereffects of fat gain. Without a diet, a person would have to ask herself if she's willing to continue to eat as an emotional coping mechanism if she has to take responsibility for what that will do to her body, having to permanently live with the weight-gain consequences. Without a diet to enable illusion that weight gain will eventually be removed, the impulse to overeat is forced to slow down.

She'd have to accept and permanently live with the consequences, which would mean she isn't a victim of her body. Her body is a victim of her unconscious rejection of uncomfortable emotions as she accepts emotional eating as a safer alternative.

Ultimately, as dieting makes food a central focus in a person's life, so do the limitations of his or her growing body. People develop such a reliance on food to manage their day-to-day emotional needs that they are stuck between 1) the anxiety about their growing weight, 2) the anxiety about eating food, and 3) the anxiety about the life stress that desperately needs food to function.

People live in constant search for food while simultaneously experiencing constant shame when they eat as there's mounting pressure to restrict food as they gain more and more weight.

As the body gets larger and larger, so do the restrictions placed on a person's life. She doesn't travel, date, exercise, pursue activities that require physical exertion, or socialize. This isolation from freedom in life and self-exploration puts even more pressure on food to replace pleasures and joys in life as the pressure increases for her to lose weight. Ultimately, the only way out is to:

1.) *Quit all forms of food morality and food restrictions that are stimulating and pressurizing the impulse to overeat.*
   Permanently removing food restrictions and allowing access to food, without guilt and shame and having to beg and plead, will remove the sparkle and "specialness" of food as it is no longer "forbidden fruit." However, the only way to truthfully surrender all forms of dieting is to accept the way your body is without expecting it will ever get better.

2.) *Accept that you will never lose weight, and that future weight gain will never get fixed, in order to reconcile the facts and truths about what will and has happened to your body.*

By accepting the truth of what has happened to your body, you are accepting responsibility for the relationship you've had with food that enabled your weight gain. Because there is nothing to excuse or fix the consequences, moving forward you'll need to awaken to and take full responsibility for the emotional bonds you've developed with food.

3.) *Address insecurity and feelings of weakness that are an inevitable consequence when giving up a co-dependent emotional relationship with food.*

As eating becomes an emotional strength when learning how to handle stresses in life, emotional confidence independent of food goes through a weakening process. Without eating you'd feel exposed, immature, weak, and in fear of situations that are perceived as too much for you to handle. This is why dieting is such an important rescuer when it comes to the need to eat emotionally.

**Diets give you a sense that you can eat freely
for emotional needs without having to accept
the consequential weight gain.**

Without a diet, you're forced to examine emotional eating. And without emotional eating, you'll have to develop a sense of emotional strength, and this requires you accept and allow your weakness to work, even if it isn't strong enough. *Ultimately, this takes courage and willingness to fail.*

If all forms of dieting, food restrictions, food judgments, and weight-loss methods are removed from being an option, a person who eats food to compensate for emotional insecurities would have to face the truth of how those dysfunctional relationships impact her body.

Diets provide the illusion that emotional eating consequences don't exist, or they don't have to be addressed because they'll eventually get fixed or taken care of.

Many people know they've gained weight and that their clothes don't fit anymore, but because they've committed to fixing those consequences "in the future," they live in a state of denial about what has happened. If they knew the accumulated weight gain was going to be permanent, would they continue to enable themselves to emotionally lean on food the same excessive way? Probably not.

> Overeating is enabled by the promise that someday the consequential weight gain will get fixed. It might not get fixed today, tomorrow, next week, or next month, but someday when life isn't so distracting and hard, the diet will be easier, and the weight gain will go away.

When wanting to emotionally eat, *but without a diet to rescue you from the resulting weight gain*, you have three choices:

1. Eat to cope and willfully accept the fat gain as a permanent consequence.
2. Refuse to eat to cope, and instead, find a new way to distract or avoid the underlying issues. Instead of eating, you find a different compulsive coping mechanism, like shopping, gambling, cleaning, etc. This type of transfer is very common when instead of facing the underlying issue, a person quits one way of coping and replaces it with another. Some

examples of how people transfer from one coping mecha-
nism to another are *by going away from:*
- ✓ Smoking, towards eating/dieting body-image controls.
- ✓ Alcoholism, towards religious controls.
- ✓ Religious controls, towards eating/dieting body-
image controls.
- ✓ Body-image eating/dieting controls, towards cleaning
and organizing controls.
- ✓ (Fill in the blanks) _____ towards _____.

3. Refuse to eat to cope, or to cope in other ways, to instead
intentionally experience the anxiety, insecurity, and sense
of weakness that develops as you face emotions that have
been avoided in fear of not being able to handle them. This
takes humility and courage.

As dieting is rejected and emotional eating is surrendered, it is inevitable that
a person will need to intentionally face the vulnerabilities of life as anybody
would when going through a strengthening and an emotional maturing
process. In the end, all of this requires that you accept the body as it is, as it
should be, and all it will be without dieting and without a dysfunctional
relationship with food.

Grieving the Loss, Acceptance, and Letting it All Go

Most people describe incredible sadness once they've come to accept the loss
of their body image and the end of their dysfunctional relationship with food.
This sadness is very different from what they experienced previously, which
was self-pity, anger, and victimhood. This sadness feels like the loss of war,
or a permanent death.

This is like realizing and admitting your marriage has failed, and that divorce
is necessary. You must let go and grieve "as it's gone," the good times and the

fantasy of what you thought the relationship could be. And despite the immense freedom and relief that comes from ending a tortured existence, there is loss, and with grief, eventually comes *acceptance*. Acceptance means you fully grasp the loss and have surrendered to it.

**When quitting all diets and forms of weight loss,
people aren't necessarily sad about the loss of those
cruel behaviors, but what they are pained about is the loss
of what these behaviors took away from them *emotionally*.**

Those who quit dieting:
- Are actually grieving safety, protection, being in spotlight, "fitting in," and a sense of purpose they thought being thinner would bring them.
- Are sad about the loss of the idea of who they wanted to be, and a life concept they thought would bring pride, confidence, joy, and freedom.
- Are mourning the only things they believed they could control and feel good about in their life.
- For many people, they are letting go of the only way of life they know and understand.

However, when they realize and clearly see they will never recover from the torment, isolation, darkness, and terror of being alone unless they also surrender the benefits, they are presented with a choice.

You could keep the known benefits of the body image, dieting, and emotional eating, but you are consciously choosing to suffer. Or you could willfully surrender the benefits, and you'll be set free *from both*. But being set free from both would open you up to vulnerability and exposure as you're presented with a new existence that is limitless and has immense freedom and independence from having to be and do what others want. This is like escaping a totalitarian religious cult, *even though you have no concept of who you are or how to function outside of it.*

This means you are leaving everything you know behind, to enter a new life you know nothing about.

SECTION 6

Letting Go

A 39-year-old Client Tells Her Story

"I started to feel bad about my body around the age of 10 due to classmates making fun of my size, which at the time was in a healthy range. I started to sneak extra snacks and desired the most-unhealthy food since *I made food the enemy*. As I got older, I tried numerous diets with my mother and friends, and was "successful" in losing 100–150 pounds three separate times. When I found myself bigger than ever and struggling to lose weight, I desperately searched YouTube for help with my binge eating disorder that I assumed I must have. Someone suggested I watch one of Robin's videos, so I took a chance listening to it."

"Through watching her videos and by working with her, I've learned that the human mind is designed to desire more food if you are telling it that food will soon become scarce when you start your diet. As long as I continue to believe that I need to lose weight, I will continue to overeat."

"My body is not actually the problem. The problem is believing the diet industry and society that encouraged me to believe that my body is the problem, and that it needs to be fixed."

"The hunger and fullness scale has helped me to not worry about when to eat or how much to eat. So much time has been wasted in the past worrying about food and which types of food are "good" or "bad," and what time of day you're expected to eat, when none of that matters as much as trusting your body to know when it's needing nutrients. It's like pressing the reset button on learning how to eat the way our bodies were meant to."

Chapter 16

The Mind of the Method

"A culture fixated on female thinness is not an obsession about female beauty. It is an obsession about female obedience."
– Naomi Wolf

Tackling Body Image Before Addressing the Hunger and Fullness Scale

If you go back through the first 200 original videos I had posted to YouTube, and compare them to the last 200 videos—all are open to the public—you will notice a big difference in the approach. My earlier videos were totally focused on the hunger and fullness scale, and figuring out a person's emotional eating triggers, one session at a time. My later videos have very little emphasis on emotional eating—and more emphasis on body image. Notice also that in more recent YouTube videos, the client I'm talking to has less emotional eating problems after we start working together, even though we spend very little time discussing food or how she eats.

Naturally, the content of the recorded YouTube sessions evolved as I made these adjustments and redirected the focus towards body image. Today, many of the clients I work with do not intend to do the hCG protocol, and I don't believe the hCG protocol is necessary for the method to work. For this reason, the approach to heal one's relationship with food, for most people, is the Mind:Body Method (without the hCG protocol).

The objective would be to first address the "Mind," or emotional aspect of the Mind:Body Method. Second, then address the Body, or physical aspect of the Method. Whether or not the participant uses the hCG protocol depends on her willingness to do it once she's indifferent about her body size and weight, and if the condition of her body is appropriate for the very low-calorie protocol without experiencing symptoms of starvation while injecting hCG.

Some people do not have enough body fat to sustain the hormonal balance necessary for the hCG in order to prevent starvation. These cases are often clients who suffer from a distorted perception that they have too much fat, when in reality they are leaner than the norm. These clients suffer from anorexic-like perceptions of their body, and are not good candidates for the hCG protocol.

Even if they have adequate fat to support the very low-calorie protocol, many people decide after they've learned and experienced eating functionally, that they will never voluntarily deprive or restrict food again.

It's not worth the risk of going back to the all-or-nothing pendulum swing between food restriction and overeating.

However, many of my clients are living with a body that has been irreparably changed by decades of chronic binge eating, dieting, and emotional eating. These clients have the typical physical symptoms for which Dr. Simeons' intended the hCG protocol as a healing therapy. With the updated Mind:Body hCG approach, once this participant has resolved the underlying emotional strain and desire to be thinner that diminishes his or her shame of being fatter, and as weight loss becomes emotionally irrelevant, then she or he would be considered a potential participant of Dr. Simeons' hCG protocol.

The "Mind" of the Method

As a person's underlying emotional strain with body fat and her emotional charge to be thinner is resolved, fear about food diminishes, and she will have an easier time discerning and relying on hunger to guide her eating. It is only then that she has a relaxed and natural environment that allows her the grace of figuring it out and learning what it's like to eat based on hunger rhythms.

The intention of the "Mind" in the Mind:Body Method is to guide a person to diminish the mind control and role that body image plays in how she relates to her life. The end goal is that she becomes indifferent about and accepts the natural conditions of her body so that her body isn't perceived as a dangerous enemy, triggering the need to diet in self-defense. Ultimately, the goal is to diminish the sense of survival safety and security attached to being thinner or any body image, and to remove the requirement of being thinner from her identity and concept of "health."

For some people, it can take over a month, sometimes two to three months, of letting go of body image before they can focus on the hunger and fullness scale. For others, letting go of body image can take a solitary moment, or it can take years. *It's a matter of whether she's suffered enough to be willing to let it go.*

When a person feels indifferent about the conditions of her body, as well as the potential weight-gain or weight-loss changes that her body will experience in life, the foundation of internal work needed to detach body image from the expectations she has for her body is complete. It is from this point a person can effectively address any residual emotional relationships with food that might still exist.

The "Mind" objectives of the Mind:Body Method are to:

1. Identify narcissistic body-image ideals and parameters you compare your body to.
2. Identify beliefs and symbolisms attached to these body-image parameters.
3. Permanently let go of the symbolisms and benefits attached to the body image.
4. Accept the body unconditionally, for what it naturally is.
5. Agree to independently navigate the freedom in your life that arises after the body image is let go.

Objective 1:

Identify narcissistic body-image ideals and parameters you compare your body to.

To identify the ideals and parameters a person uses to compare her body to, first there must be *an understanding of what body image is.* The traditional understanding of body image is that it is a mental image in your mind of the body you want, typically represented by what others see as positive. With body image, typically the way the body is seen, whether positive or negative, is used to define the worth of that person. If people like the condition of your body, you are a more valuable person. If people don't like your body, you are a less valuable person.

The idea is that a positively seen body reflects a positive inner-self.

As though opinions about the body—its function, abilities, and its looks—can be used with symbolism to define our intrinsic value as a human, as well as the quality and character of the people we are. In order to form a body image in the mind, first there must be a parameter, or set of parameters that are believed to be ideal, from which the body is compared to. These ideals are dogmatic—set in place by some authority, unquestionably defining and promoting what they believe is superior for people to aspire for and to achieve.

For many people the ideal is a long and lean picture of thinness, where bones are visible, which is represented by the models in fashion magazines or seen on the runway. Some people idealize the fitness body with muscles and ultra-leanness that shows muscular definition and strength. Others seek the ideals of beauty defined by larger breasts, a small waist, and a large butt. They often also idealize makeup and accentuated lips and eyelashes.

> **No matter what the parameters of their chosen body-image ideal, the idea is the same: *when you achieve the ideal you are a better, more valuable superior human.* For this reason, when a person believes and internalizes a body image, she assumes that when she reaches the goal, she will feel better about herself—especially around others.**

It could be a smaller waist, a lower weight, a specific size of clothing, or fitting into an old pair of jeans they used to be able to wear. It could be a certain amount of time on the treadmill, or an ability to do a specific number of pull-ups. Whatever the ideal, there are parameters used to measure how her body compares. When a person gets closer to achieving these parameters, she can experience a sense of accomplishment, or confidence. For some, the person thinks she needs these accomplishments to improve her self-esteem.

Many people confuse self-esteem with body image. Because body image is assumed to be a direct reflection of your quality as a person, people think they are confident in themselves when they reach these standards. The truth is that they aren't confident in themselves, but are instead confident in the body image they're complying to. This isn't "self"-esteem but rather "body-image"-esteem.

I've had many clients feel at peace with their body at a larger than socially accepted weight. I've also had clients whose body matches the ideal ultra-lean body image who are severely ashamed with minor weight increases.

> **The discontent a person has with her body
> isn't just measured by the difference
> between what she has and what she wants,
> but it is also magnified by the importance,
> need, and strictness of how she holds
> herself to the ideal.**

Ask yourself:
- ☐ What are your body image parameters and ideals?
- ☐ Describe the picture in your mind of the body you want?
- ☐ Where and who did you learn these ideals from?
- ☐ What would change in your life if those parameters and ideals no longer applied to you?

Objective 2:

**Identify beliefs and symbolisms attached
to these body-image parameters.**

The confidence people attach in their mind to achieving the ideal body image is based on symbolism. These parameters are given meaning as if to non-verbally communicate, or give a hint about, a person's inner quality or worth. It's as if the way a person looks can tell you if she is a safe or risky person. Body image is used to make assumptions about a variety of human qualities and risks.

After years of study, I created this list of some of the commonly discussed qualities of what thinness symbolizes, and consequently what being fatter symbolizes:

QUALITY	THINNESS	FATNESS
• Work ethic	Works hard	Lazy
• Intelligence	Smart	Dumb
• Cleanliness	Clean	Dirty
• Trustworthiness	Honest	Dishonest
• Sexuality	Sexual	Abstinent
• Health	Healthy	Diseased
• Physical	Comfortable	Uncomfortable
• Ability	Unlimited	Limited
• Emotional strength	Strong	Weak
• Dedication	Focused	Distracted
• Reliability	Reliable	Unreliable
• Resilience	Can handle challenge	*Cannot* handle challenge
• Kindness	Critical	Loving
• Lenience	Strict	Laid back
• Fun	Stick in the mud	Fun!
• Loving	Judgmental	Forgiving

In general, a culture that promotes being thinner as superior and of a higher quality will assume that being fatter is inferior and of lower quality. Even though people who have more body fat tend to be viewed as easier going, more loving, and more fun, there is stigma attached to having more body fat—that when its internalized can negatively impact how a person feels about him or herself.

Stigma is having a bad reputation, disgraced, or looked down upon for having some negative quality. Stigma assumes the person, as a whole being, is inherently a lower quality or defective. With that in mind, when a person believes in body-image dogma, and fears the resulting stigma for not complying, it would be understandable why a person would assume that by losing weight, she would feel better about herself. The question is: Why aren't people questioning the stigma? Is it really true?

In order to question the stigma, you'd have to question the dogma that defines what the truth is. *Dogma is an unquestionable truth given to you by an authority.* In this case, the dogma is given to you by a thin-supremacy cultural belief that thinner people are better people. Similar to other narcissistic belief systems, like white supremacy, this belief system assumes that thinner people are superior people and therefore, fatter people are inferior. With dogma, you are not to question whether what they say is true. Therefore, if you are fatter, you have no choice but to think your body isn't good enough, and to battle your weight in order to feel better about yourself socially.

The truth is that there wouldn't be negative inferior attachments to fatness if there weren't positive, narcissistic symbolism attached to thinness.

From there, the body is compared to the thinner/superior look held in mind. The difference or similarity between what is idealized and what a person actually has, promotes a spectrum of either pride or shame attached to her body. *Once someone has internalized a body-image belief, it then becomes un-noticeable— like brainwashing. What is noticed, however, is how it makes her feel about her-self.* When her body more closely matches the ideal image, she feels safer and more confident. When her body is further away from the ideal image, she feels insecure and vulnerable.

Most people are totally unaware that they are identifying their worth and value based on symbolic body images, especially when their family and friends are doing the same.

- If your parents value their thinness and promote food restriction, you will too.
- If they feel ashamed about their weight, and perpetually talk about how bad they feel about eating, you will too.
- If you hear others being constantly criticized or praised

based on their looks, it will be internalized as important information that you should be aware of within yourself and others, *at all time.*

Many people wanting to lose weight are actually seeking the desire to feel lovable. Women have come to me seeking help with emotional eating—thinking they need to lose weight so that their husband will stop cheating. They think that by losing weight their spouse will love them more, or that losing weight will give them an opportunity to find a soulmate. They want to lose the negative stigma associated to having more body fat in order to achieve the positive benefits of what being thinner and more superior will bring them.

Typically, body images symbolize being lovable or worthy of love. For many people, achieving a body image is about getting others to love and appreciate who you are. However, for many of the clients I've worked with who suffered with the most excruciating shame and resulting eating disorders, it is about feeling lovable *to themselves.* They want to feel good in their mind about themselves, and without being thinner, they don't want to associate with their body. I believe this is a survival mechanism directly tied to the need, as pack animals, to feel that we have something to contribute—*to feel that we are lovable.*

But if a person thinks her body threatens her lovability, she'll treat it like it's a threat. Despite the fact that her body is giving her life, consciousness, and all the senses that allow her to experience the world around her, she treats her body as if it's a predator threatening and destroying her life. She becomes a victim of her body, and her body is perceived as her persecutor.

In order to recover, a person must surrender the body image that has symbolized being lovable, but that has also defined her natural body as shameful and worthy of isolation. *This is the most excruciating and difficult part of recovery.*

Objective 3:

**Permanently surrender and let go of the symbolisms
and benefits attached to the body image.**

Giving up goals that symbolize acceptance, being loved, and the idea you'll
be included isn't how our brain and instincts evolved. We evolved to do whatever we can to gain inclusion into our family and tribe as a way to secure our
survival. "Fitting in" is the entire premise of Maslow's third hierarchy of need.
Although, when the culture you are trying to assimilate into promotes body
images that threaten and strain your psychological wellbeing—to the point
you might be suffering with an eating disorder—the only way to recover is
to give up the security that body image apparently provides.

Once a person sees that her devotion and effort is far beyond what anyone
should be expected to do in order to "fit in," she sees that her failure and inadequacy is worthy of compassion, understanding, and forgiveness. Given
the context of the unrealistic and inhumane standards of the thin-supremacy
belief systems, she doesn't deserve to live in shame or be defined by the suffering she lived while supporting that narcissistic cultural ideology.

Therefore, in order for a person to escape the controls of her impulse to
strictly diet and emotionally eat, it's inevitable she'll have to permanently
surrender the symbolism of strength attached to her body image and eating,
as well as all hope that she'll ever be thinner in order to expose the weakness
she feels within herself.

**When controlling access to food is what has
kept you safe and hidden from exposure, letting
go of the benefits attached to body image
and the disordered eating can literally
feel as if you're going to die.**

By letting these standards and symbolisms go, you are essentially letting go of your survival. This must be accepted too. The risk of leaving the safety and predictability of a life you already know to then enter a new life you might be too weak to handle, and one you have no clue about—feels like suicide for many people.

Facing the exposure and terror without turning to a form of self-defense, even though you have no sense of strength to handle it, takes an incredible amount of humility and courage.

> **The willingness to accept the truth, even when
> it comes with excruciating psychological pain,
> is a powerful act of faith, especially when
> there is no sense of what life will be
> like, or if you'll survive that pain.**

If you are independently willing to humbly face, accept, and experience your inner sense of weakness as the truth of your capacity to handle life, no matter how pitiful and nonexistent it feels, the threats of not being lovable or not surviving lose their power. Once you've let go of body image and willfully faced rejection, abandonment, and a life being alone, you're going to have to redefine how you want to relate to your body and to life.

Ask yourself:
- ☐ Do you want to dislike your body?
- ☐ Do you want to have to change it before you allow yourself to start living?
- ☐ More importantly, what is the true genetic predisposition of your body if you were to completely stop all dieting, exercise, and emotional eating?
- ☐ Are you willing to find out the true nature of your body, even if it doesn't match what is culturally accepted?

Objective 4:

Accept the body unconditionally, for what it naturally is.

The goal of the fourth objective is to unconditionally accept whatever that body is. The only way you will be free from having to fix your body, is if you accept the body for what it truthfully is, and stop altering it to be thinner with some form of disordered eating behavior.

This means you would have to accept what happens if you stop excessively exercising, stop counting calories or measuring your food, stop reading food labels, stop eating to escape uncomfortable emotions, and stop any form of justified or reasoned restrictions or eating in excess.

There are five ways the body must be accepted in a culture that worships thinness:

1. You must accept that you'll never again be thinner than you are.
- This requires you give up the shelter that being thinner provides you from judgment, and that you surrender the narcissistic pride, aspirations, fantasies, and dreams of life in a thinner body.
- All the times you allowed yourself to binge eat only because you assumed the weight gain would eventually get fixed, *will never get fixed.*
- Clothes you purchased when you were thinner will need to be sifted through, boxed up, sold, or given away.
- This might also mean you have to give up what you thought being thinner would give you: the spotlight, potential marital relationships or security, children, travel, easier mobility, and the idea you'd be healthier if you could be thinner.
- **By giving this up, you are essentially giving up any reason to diet now or in the future.**

2. *In order to accept that you'll never be thinner, you'll have to accept your current weight, as it is, with all of its vulnerabilities, discomforts, and faults.*

- This means you'll have to accept what has happened to your body as a result of bingeing, even though you wouldn't have binged if you knew the weight gain would never get fixed.
- To accept your current body, you'd have to take responsibility for how your relationship with food has impacted your body, and that the physical discomfort you might be living with as a consequence of your dysfunctional relationship with food, *will never get fixed.*
- You'll have to accept your fears of being stigmatized, seen as a failure, are worthless to society, and that you might end up being alone.
- **By accepting your current size and weight, you are essentially giving up any reason to diet now or in the future.**

3. *You must accept that your body might gain body fat and naturally be larger than the cultural ideal or what is deemed "healthy."*

- For people who are anorexic and/or bulimic, it is inevitable that you must accept the truth of the genetics handed down to you from you parents, your grandparents, and thousands of years of generations before you.
- For people who emotionally eat, without a diet you'll have to accept the inevitable weight gain as the consequence. Without disordered dieting and eating, you'll have to face the truth of your natural body, and that truth is probably bigger than the body you want.
  - ✓ If the body you want requires obsessive/compulsive starvation, exercise, and purging to attain, it's a sure guarantee you'll gain weight by letting go of these disordered behaviors.

219

✓ If you hold onto dysfunctional eating as an emotional crutch, it is guaranteed your body will have to gain fat to sustain your life.

✓ Accepting that you'll gain weight means you'll have to buy comfortable clothes that fit, and that **by accepting the risks and fact that you will gain weight, you are essentially giving up any reason to diet now or in the future**.

4. *If your body is naturally thinner, you must be indifferent about it, without attaching pride or narcissistic value to it.*

- The goal is indifference to weight loss so that there's nothing good or bad about it.

- Even if you're given praise or compliments on your body, the goal is that these opinions, whether positive or negative, don't impact how you relate to your body.

- This doesn't mean you can't notice or appreciate physical relief that occurs for some people with weight loss, but that you don't internalize it as a symbol of your worth.

- It's the body's business if it naturally loses body fat, and if you attach to it, get too excited, inflate yourself with pride, or take credit for it as a source of egotistical supply, all of the disordered eating and fixation on your weight, pressure to diet, and the desire to eat excessively will return.

- One way to think about this is that you are committing to never use weight loss or thinness with the intent to gain favor with friends, family, or strangers. You don't want your body image to be how you secure self-esteem or a positive relationship with others.

- **By not caring about fat loss, you are essentially giving up on any reason to diet now or in the future.**

5. If your body naturally loses weight, you must be willing to regain that weight.

- This means any lost weight you've attached pride and success to, might be regained if you give up the methods used for that weight loss.
- The goal is *total indifference to your natural body size, shape, and weight.* If you gain weight, no big deal. If you lose weight, so what? If your body stays the same, that's okay too. None of it matters, and all of it is good if that's what the body naturally does without forceful influence from bingeing, emotional eating, excessive exercise, dieting, or any imposed efforts to lose weight.
- If you can accept that at any time your body could lose and regain weight because its allowed to regulate itself, **you are essentially giving up any reason to diet now or in the future.**

By giving up the body image, you're also giving up the pride, shame, and pressure to be defined by it from every angle. *Without body image the pride of thinness wouldn't exist, and neither would the shame of fatness.* This means there's no point to the desire behind being thinner, losing weight, or preventing weight gain—which permanently ends your relationship with dieting and food restrictions—as well as frequently checking your body, and also needing to monitor your weight.

Ultimately, when giving up a body image you are giving up an identity or a self-concept. You are surrendering a life you know so well in order to start a new life you know nothing about. And until you surrender the martyr role and the victim position, you will continue to defend, rationalize, and argue for the benefits of the disorder that keep you coming back despite the isolation, darkness, abuse, and misery that you want to escape.

When you willfully hand over the benefits of the body image and dieting, you will need to grieve the loss.

Objective 5:

**Agree to independently navigate the vulnerability
and freedom in your life that arises after the body image,
dieting, and emotional eating is let go.**

Instead of hiding and fighting in self-defense, accept the truth of your body in exchange for freedom, even if it is seen as inferior. This freedom allows you to experience life from a new perspective—to see that your authentic value and ability to live isn't made better or worse when praised or judged by others when you're compared to self-"concepts" defined by a narcissistic culture.

- The courage it takes to independently accept one's true self is the foundation of self-confidence, which opens the mind to curious wonderment, creativity, innovation, and exploration in life.
- Because the pressure to perform, please others, and to succeed at all cost is gone, the truth of one's capacity in life can be discovered and set free to flourish.
- With open mindedness, there is no need to control the outcomes of life, which means there is more willingness to take risks.

**It is at this point that a person transcends the crippling
forces of self-preservation to experience a different
liberated way the mind works. Even though you have
no sense of what will come to be, a new existence presents
itself. It is free, open, and hard for many people to describe.**

When freedom arises, the goal is to take the reins to independently define the worth of your life, and what you want out of it, even when you might feel too immature and weak to know what you want or like. You'll need to accept that truth about what you want out of life, even when others might not agree with it, without thinking there's something wrong with you or feeling bad about it. Moving forward, you'll need to take responsibility for expressing the nature of your true self, and make decisions for what is right and truthful to you.

Taking ownership of your life comes with freedom and infinite possibilities, no different than a toddler starting life. Just as a young child learns the ins-and-outs of life, no matter what age you are when you choose independence, you too must learn the ins-and-outs of the freedom of who you are and what you want with the life you're living. And just as a child will be criticized when he or she doesn't match societal dogmas, you too must be open to being judged, ridiculed, bullied, and rejected when you honor yourself over the body-image dogma from which you're seeking liberation.

The good news is that you get to do this as an adult who already understands how the society you live in works, and what true and real dangers do exist. You don't have to start over as a child, or have to live through the awkward-ness and misery of junior high and adolescence all over again to get to this place of maturity and freedom. You have enough knowledge and wisdom to navigate the culture we live in, without taking it as seriously.

One way to describe this is that you are living "in" society, not "of" society. This means you can adapt and assimilate into culture, but culture doesn't become who you are, how you identify yourself, or how you define your worth. This allows you to be a human anthropologist, and to adapt to an ever-changing life that is always evolving in order to continue to learn, grow, and create and recreate what you want as your life progresses.

The goal is to recognize that you have good integrity, and that you've always done the best you could with what you were aware of. And what you were aware of was to do what others told you. Now, you are aware that maybe this wasn't the best thing for you physically or emotionally.

Chapter 17

The Body of the Method

"If hunger is not the problem, then eating is not the solution."
– Author Unknown

Eating in Radical Abundance

Today, food is easy to get, in any quantity, and is relatively affordable for most people. The ability to cope and hide from our fears and stresses with food has become an easy distraction—especially in a culture that pushes food restrictions while at the same time living in that abundance.

As people have relied on dieting and food restrictions to guide their eating, they've also triggered famine mechanisms while food is available and abundant around them.

This has enabled people who diet to develop an emotional reliance on food in order to give themselves temporary relief from the survival strains of dieting.

Over time, as they develop a connection between certain emotions and the freedom to eat, they become more and more emotionally reliant on eating to cope with the vulnerabilities of life. As a result, they weaken their innate sense of self-esteem and tolerance for life's normal stress. Food becomes a central focus and need in life for emotional reasons, and at the same time food is perceived as a threat for physical reasons.

When I ask clients how they'd eat if there weren't any forms of diet regulation or restrictions, most people respond that they'd be afraid they wouldn't know what to do. They assume that if given access to the available abundance of food around them, they'd eat excessively without end. They're afraid when given access to food they won't know when to stop. However, this fear arises based on their history and what they've experienced in their past with eating compulsions that stem from the severity of their diet's restrictions and rules.

As the thin-supremacy body images are surrendered, so are biased needs for dieting, as well as the artificial threats and dangers to a person's first hierarchy of survival needs. Without the diet regulation, these survival mode impulses to secure food melt away.

As dieting and fear-based food judgments and restrictions about food are removed, *there are no rules and regulations that dogmatically decide:*
- How much or how little you should eat.
- The timing of when you should and shouldn't eat.
- What foods are "safe" or "dangerous," "good" or "bad," or "right" or "wrong" to eat.

By eliminating these regulations, a person:
- Doesn't need to use emotional reasons to negotiate, plead, and bargain with the diet rules for why she deserves access to food.
- Doesn't need emotional eating to serve as a break from the strain of diets.

- No longer has rules that when broken, lead to feelings of failure, loss, and shame. Without dieting rules, there is nothing to "break" or ruin.

- Doesn't have a way to fix consequential weight gain that occurs as a result from emotionally driven eating. There's nothing to enable the emotionally codependent nature of emotional eating by taking away the consequences. There's no "fall guy" to fix the physical impact and weight gain that occurs when eating is negotiated for emotional reasons. This means that if she chooses to eat to hide from an emotional challenge, she is accepting the physical consequence *as a permanent result,* putting her into a position to recognize her response comes at a cost.

- Doesn't have to eat more or eat available food all at once in fear she won't get more. The food isn't going away, and more is always available. There's no future or anticipated deprivation around the corner that triggers a need to eat just because it's available. For example, just because peanuts or pretzels are offered when flying in an airplane, that doesn't mean you have to eat them right then and there. You can get pretzels and peanuts any time you want, which makes them less "special."

When body image is surrendered, there is no reason for weight loss-oriented deprivations and food regulation. Without those regulations, many people feel incredible liberation, but that freedom comes with open abundance of food that saturates our current modern society.

Without a diet to regulate and direct when, how much, and what you can and cannot eat, a person is left to figure out how she's going to eat moving forward. Besides teaching a person to look at how she'd eat if she had to ration her food, I also teach her to eat as if she is given permanent access to "the table of abundance."

The Table of Abundance

Imagine that you win the lottery, and you purchase a large mansion for your family to live in for the rest of your life. In this mansion is a huge dining hall with chefs from around the world cooking for you daily. In the dining hall is a very long table that could host over 100 people, and on this table are overflowing amounts of food. There are fruits and vegetables of every variety, breads, pastries, cakes, pies, pastas, chocolates, candy, lentils, rice, seafood, and meats and cheeses of every kind from all over the globe. Whatever you want is there every day, all day long, in endless quantity for the rest of your life. I call this the "table of abundance." It is overflowing and will stay that way for centuries to come.

When I describe this table to clients, I get a couple of reactions. Most of the time people feel a little overwhelmed and grossed out by the excessive richness of the table. They immediately feel a calm separation occur as they realize that the food is there every day, all the time, and that it gets restocked as soon as something is eaten. There's a sense of separation that occurs as they don't have to think about food or hold food in their mind as a central focus any more. If they know they can choose whatever they want when they need it, they don't have to worry about it, and they don't have to waste their day stressed about whether there's going to be enough.

A less-common initial response when I describe the table of abundance is pure excitement, but that excitement subsides as they realize that the food would eventually lose its appeal. At first, some people assume they'd spend all day every day eating as their central focus, and because of that they assume this table of abundance is a bad thing. However, when they truthfully imagine what would actually happen, they realize the food on the table of abundance allows them to relax as its availability has no end. The food and the perpetual abundance on the table loses its "specialness."

I ask each person how her life would change and what she'd do with her time if she had such overflowing abundance at her fingertips, forever. Most people feel great relief knowing that with that type of food security, they'd relax about food and let their minds be liberated to focus on other things. Eating would be exciting only when they were hungry.

Without hunger, they'd find other things to do with their energy and time because they'd know that when it's time to eat, the food will be available in all its variety and plenty. They won't miss out, not get any, or go hungry. And because the overflowing abundance will be available for the rest of their life, there's no pressure to eat as much as they can in one sitting because it will be available the next time they're hungry—for the rest of their life. Eating one item doesn't mean they'll never get a different item or are missing out. Everything on the table will be available again and again and again, day after day after day. If there's pizza available every day, it doesn't make sense to eat it excessively thinking that you won't have enough or can't get it later.

The emotional reasoning behind overeating loses power.

When I bring up emotionally based eating in regard to the table of abundance, people recognize the unusual nature of emotional eating when food is always abundant and available without needing to beg for it.

Unless there is a true famine, or foreseen loss of food in the near future, any bargaining to excessively eat at the table of abundance when there isn't any hunger or physical need would be a clear indication of an emotional problem.

And because there is no diet or reinforced food judgments and restrictions, the choice to excessively eat for emotional reasons comes with accepting full responsibility for the resultant weight gain and physical consequences.

When access to food is fully and completely safe and secure for the long-foreseen future, the need to eat based on survival-securing impulses goes away. The relaxed and less forceful need to eat for hunger and pleasure become a stronger motivation, and all of the energy and focus that you used to fixate on food and food restraints, is freed up to explore other possibilities in life.

The freedom that opens up when dieting and food aren't the main priority or central focus in life leaves people at a loss for what to do with their time, mind, and energy. This freedom is why many people sabotage their own efforts to change, even though the result is both more suffering, and living a predictable life they know harms them. Holding onto old patterns of thought that sensationalize emotional reward from studying diets or eating as entertainment make the recovery process very difficult. For most people, the creative process is difficult because it requires that you let go of old ways of thinking to create something new.

To do this, you have to create new hobbies and find new ways to entertain yourself that don't require eating. If eating, over-exercising, or studying diets weren't an option, what would you do to fill your time? Would you start or finish a project?

For many people, once body image, dieting and excessive food consumption are removed from their life, they feel as if they're young children learning whom they are and how to live again. And learning how to eat without a mental concept regulating their food consumption can seem scary—especially when dieting and food controls have dictated their relationship with food and directed how they should eat for most of their life. *However, as body image is removed from the equation, a person has the space and grace to learn and figure it out.*

Without having the pressure to regulate her body fat, there's no stress, pressure, or perfectionism demanding she strictly diet without lenience. From there she has a tension-free environment to learn her body and the physical cues it sends as a way to regulate when food is physiologically needed. With time and practice she can reconnect with her physical sense of hunger and satiation, to naturally guide when and how much she should eat, freeing her energy and mind from having to mentally manage it.

How to Eat Without a Body Image or Diet

As the desires diminish that are driving the need to lose weight and prevent weight gain, a person emotionally relaxes about food. Then her priority is to learn the sensations of hunger and fullness, and how to distinguish the physical need for food from her emotional desires to eat or diet. This often leaves people at a loss for how to eat and relate to food.

> **They previously related to food with such emotional charge that eating was never about physical need.** *Eating had been either about punishment or reward.*

To have a neutral relationship with food can feel foreign and you feel vulnerable. Many people describe this freedom with food as juvenile, or elementary—as if they are learning to live again, like the fresh start of a child. At this point, hunger and fullness becomes an important securing aspect of the body that guides the physical need for food. This is very different than the mental controlling-ness that diets previously imposed on the body.

The ability to identify the inherent sense of hunger and satiety/overindulgence, and the ability to discern psychological hunger from physical hunger, is fundamental for living free of dieting, deprivation, and emotional eating. When the hunger and fullness scale is truthfully followed, a more dynamic, adaptable, and functional way of eating—one that requires minimal effort can be experienced—especially when there is no famine, scarcity, or feelings of badness attached to food. This is the premise of the "Body" of the Mind:Body Method.

As discussed in *Weight-Loss Apocalypse-1,* the "Body" objectives of the
Mind:Body Method are to:

1. Identify stages of physical satiation or complete fullness.
2. Identify states of physical hunger.
3. Differentiate mental hunger from physical hunger.
4. Identify triggers that prompt mental hunger and emotion-
    ally validate eating.
5. Allow discomfort without justification or action.
6. Eat based on physical need, reconditioning functional eat-
    ing in uncontrolled situations.

The "Body" objectives of the Mind:Body Method are an approach to eating
that reacquaints an individual with her body's natural hunger and fullness
regulation, without the stress and anxiety of having to control one's weight.
This is similar to how we allow the body to regulate when and how much we
urinate. We don't necessarily tell the body to urinate on a schedule, and we
don't monitor the chemicals and toxins released from the body, or tell the
body how much total urination should occur in a day. Why not give the
body a similar freedom to regulate when and how much we eat?

The Hunger-and-Fullness Scale

The hunger-and-fullness scale gives people a clean backdrop to recognize the
difference between physical need and the emotional drive to restrict or indulge.
Learning these cues, and understanding what they mean, is an important step
toward living without the need for diets, and the consequential impulses to
overeat.

Here again, as you read earlier in the book, is a description of each number
on the hunger-and-fullness scale.

Hunger is described in terms of urgency,
and *fullness* in terms of physical sensation.

The Hunger Scale

1. *Disparaging.* Hunger is actually subsiding, as you feel less energy, less focus, and less desire for movement. Your headache continues, you feel lightheaded, and your stomach might have an acidic feeling. You're a bit cold, and your posture is lazy and rounded. You feel shaky, and a bit nauseous.

2. *Critical.* You have anger, irritability, your head hurts, and you don't care what food you eat as long as it's in large quantity—and fast (you're craving starches and sugars, combined with fat).

3. *Urgent.* You're uncomfortable, and you should have eaten ten minutes ago. Search for food is now imminent, as hunger is increasingly urgent, and choice of food is becoming less rational. Fast food is very appealing, and the wait time at traditional restaurants seem less tolerable.

4. *Patient.* You're hungry, but can wait a bit. This is a good time to start prepping food for a meal. Most people can tolerate the wait in a restaurant at this point.

5. *Content.* You feel nothing, perfectly comfortable with or without food. Hunger is completely gone, with no sense of urgency.

The Fullness Scale

6. *Satisfaction.* You are confident your hunger is gone. You are feeling good.

7. *Satiation.* You're feeling a bit too satisfied, burping, and feeling some discomfort in the belly. Because you have no hunger, continuing to eat would mean that you've justified

it emotionally. This is usually when a dieter feels guilty, and may defend a compensatory binge.

8. *Full.* You're uncomfortable, and definitely feeling your stomach. There's still some room for food because your stomach hasn't started to stretch yet. Will need to wait three or more hours until your next meal.

9. *Discomfort.* You're very full, and feeling sick. Stomach is distended, with no more room for anything. Perhaps you have indigestion and a headache, and wish to lie down to reduce discomfort.

10. *Pain.* You've eaten so much you're contemplating inducing yourself to vomit in order to relieve the physical pain. You have to unbutton the first button on your pants, and can hardly stand to move. You're tired and need to take a nap, making it feel like being "Thanksgiving full."

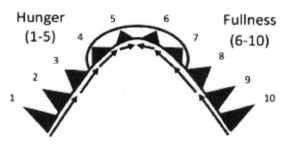

Hunger and Fullness Scale

This scale does not determine how fast one goes from feeling level one number (disparaging) to the next. How quickly hunger elevates depends on the individual, and how much fat he or she has relative to stress and activity level. The same goes for how long a person goes without feeling hunger, and how much food a person needs to feel satisfied.

Many who have significantly more body fat don't feel hunger much at all, but when the physical urge to eat presents itself, hunger manifests rapidly and intensely. When food is eaten, it takes only small amounts of food, and satiation can last for longer periods of time.

For those who have less fat, it could take more time to adjust to hunger, but more food is needed to feel satisfied. This shows that with less fat, more food must be eaten to adequately stimulate enough leptin to desensitize the urge-to-eat message that's sent from the brain.

Hunger is the communication to the conscious mind when food is hormonally necessary—and when it is not. In order to relearn the body's regulatory signals to eat, its imperative people pay attention to discern true hunger from mentally constructed diets and emotional desires to eat.

**The goal is not to wait so long that you get too hungry—
and not to eat too much so that you're overly full.**

In general, the goal is to start eating around 3.5 on the hunger scale, and stop eating around a 6 on the fullness scale. There is no "perfect" way of eating to hunger and fullness.

The "Body" of the Mind:Body Method Objectives

The "body" objectives of the Mind:Body Method are an approach to eating that reacquaints an individual with her body's natural regulation of hunger and fullness, without the stress and anxiety of having to control her size, weight, and perceived "health." The idea is to allow the body to do that job, and you then follow its lead.

**You allow the body to guide when
and how much you should eat.**

This is similar to how we allow the body to regulate when and how much we urinate. We get a physical sensation with a sense of timeliness and urgency.

When you first get the feeling you need to urinate, you don't necessarily need to go right then and there. We have the ability to override that sensation and wait until it's the right time with the appropriate privacy. The longer you wait, the more pressure you feel, and the more urgent the signal is in your mind. The hunger and the physical sensation guiding when you should eat *are similar.*

If there was a "urinating diet" regulating when and how much you should urinate, you'd have to ignore your body's natural signal, to instead mentally monitor conditions set by the system dictating a predictable pattern of urination. This sounds ridiculous, but when you look at the physical signals of hunger as an inborn regulation similar to urination, diets also seem ridiculous.

We don't necessarily tell the body to urinate on a schedule, and then monitor the chemicals and toxins released from the body, or tell the body how much total urination should occur in a day. Why not give the body a similar freedom to regulate when and how much we eat? However, as people have relied on dieting regulation to control when, what, and how much they can and cannot eat, they've lost touch with these signals and how food affects them.

The goal of this process is to first learn how the body signals and regulates the need for food, and second, to identify eating that is based on emotional needs that have nothing to do with physical need. Ultimately, as a person relaxes and allows her body to lead in guiding when and how much to eat, she will be free from regulating diets and mentally judging food that directs how to eat, and also free from relating to food in a dysfunctional way as emotional support.

1. **Identify stages of satiation and complete fullness:** On the fullness scale, this would be identifying 6, 7, 8, 9, and 10. Clearly differentiating a 5 from a 6 and 7 is imperative in relearning what it means when there's enough leptin

communicating when food is no longer needed hormonally, and when to stop eating (no matter what the serving size is.)

Relearning to understand physical signals and signs of satiation (removed from an emotional drive) is an integral part of the Mind:Body Method. For people who are compelled and conditioned to eat based on emotions or strict adherence to rules of a diet, *fullness is either linked to shame resulting in an emotional binge, or it's linked to a sense of security and freedom from the rigidity of the diet.* When forced to eat to full capacity without emotional validation, the physical detriment is much easier to identify. The goal here is to allow yourself to eat to fullness without needing to justify or rationalize it.

We recommend you choose days where overeating doesn't make sense at all. Refrain from this allowed overeating at a birthday party or a cultural holiday feast. Try not to have a good reason to force-feed, and this will help you relearn the body's signals separate from the dysfunctional drive.

2. **Identify stages of physical hunger**: Using the hunger scale, urgency to eat is identified using numbers 1, 2, 3, 4, and 5. This range of hunger goes from feelings of nothing (5) to complete loss of concentration, irritability, and painfully intense hunger (1). Clearly understanding the difference between 3 and 4 is critical in relearning the communication that leptin provides as a signal for when the body needs food hormonally, and when to start eating.

For many, they have never felt hunger. In fact, it is not uncommon for people to think that hunger is when they no longer feel full. On the other hand, some people have learned to associate hunger with fear, or power, or control. The goal here, similar to discerning fullness, is to detach any emotional meaning or symbolism from the sensation of hunger. Relearning to recognize these physical signals, along with the true feelings of hunger, is also vital in relearning to eat and gaining independence from the rigid concepts defined by a diet and justified emotional eating.

3. **Differentiate mental hunger from physical hunger:** The more aware you are of your body's physical cues of hunger and sensations of fullness, the more obvious emotional justifications to control food and eating become— whether it's eating when you have no hunger, trying to eat less than the body needs, or continuing to eat after hunger is gone. What I love about this concept is that it's completely individualized and tailored to your body. This eliminates judgment towards both food and rules that are difficult to apply.

During this process, mental hunger becomes clear as the goals are less about weight and more about identifying habits, emotions, and dysfunctional ideals centered on eating and food. When physical hunger is clearly defined (removed from fear of eating and emotional drive) mental appetite and hunger are distinguishable and brought to the forefront of consciousness. This allows the participant to choose to evaluate where the mental hunger came from, and to choose not to eat when there is no physical need.

This can occur not only before a person eats, but often after a person starts eating. She can be hungry when she starts eating, but as hunger subsides and sensations of satiation and fullness appear, the desire to eat for emotional reasons can arise. Deciphering the urge to reason, rationalize, justify, and argue for food occurs as it is clear the body no longer needs food.

4. **Identify triggers that prompt mental hunger and emotionally validated eating:** Some people know exactly why they eat, but they may not realize why it's emotionally rationalized. These are the triggers that create mental appetite and emotional hunger.

   For most, eating compensates for feelings of insecurity that is created by doubt in their ability to handle emotions independently without food. I've frequently observed that these impulses often stem from feelings of being powerless, or a victim to some experience. Whatever the trigger, if no physical need exists, the mental hunger requires some form of validation to justify giving in to the dependent feeling.

   Once hunger and fullness are recognized, and the urge to justify dieting or overeating is clear, the goal is to do nothing in order to create a new perspective that gives people the confidence to process emotions independently—without food or the impulse to diet. This approach motivates people to open their minds to vulnerability—in order to intentionally test emotional independence.

5. **Allow discomfort without justification or action.** For many, the emotional insecurity that brings about vulnerability feels unbearable. Letting go of an eating behavior that has felt emotionally important and rewarding can be extremely frustrating.

Many people eat without physical hunger, telling themselves that their body will fix what happens. But at the same time, once their emotional needs to eat have been satisfied, they get discouraged that they didn't lose as much weight. To avoid the discomfort that eating protects them from, people often take advantage of any grey area the hunger and fullness scale allows. However, when the truth is that they have no hunger—this makes emotional eating very obvious to the observer.

During the process people should seek to understand how they would eat if there wasn't a food or a diet to control or rescue them. The goal is to invite vulnerable discomfort rather than to justify removing it. Instead of eating, they must learn to acknowledge their body is in control, and if you're hungry, you will eat…but if you're not hungry, you won't eat.

For this to work it is imperative you hold yourself responsible to tell the truth.

If you want freedom from emotional eating and dieting, you have to be willing to experience what you have hid from with those behaviors.

This concept is foreign to what's been taught to most of us since childhood—using band aids, pacifiers, and any object to change and distract ourselves from uncomfortable feelings. Removing a food and "dieting pacifiers" from artificially helping strengthen you emotionally requires initial feelings of weakness and temporary discomfort, but in the end this experience and internal reflection about it allows for a completely new perspective and a "rebooting" of the mind and body. The goal here is *to surrender all justifications to find the truth.* It is to intentionally test emotional independence without eating or dieting.

6. **Eat based on physical need, reconditioning functional eating in any uncontrolled situation:** Once there's a new sense of emotional autonomy, it's important to test functional eating in the real world of abundance. Building confidence in one's ability to sense hunger and eat various types of food (in different environments) is vital in the process towards emotional independence. Functional application of hunger and fullness, when huge quantities of uncontrolled food options are available, is the ultimate physical and emotional success.

   The goal is to allow yourself access to all food in large amounts, and to rely on your physical sense of hunger to guide when and how much you should eat. Unfortunately, when a diet's restraint is considered as a necessary part of emotional control, people can go through an all-or-nothing emotional pendulum swing when a diet isn't available.

Vulnerability, without direct suggestions for what, and how much to eat, can make the transition from a controlled diet to freedom to eat at the "table of abundance" feel undisciplined and overwhelming.

When there's no diet, no boundaries, and no clear rules about how to eat, a person can lack confidence in her emotional strength. Avoiding vulnerability and temptation keeps her weak to sense emotions independently, and removes the opportunity to learn to enjoy food functionally.

It's not that we shouldn't like or take pleasure in food, but that we should become skilled at eating without making diet controls or compensatory excessiveness the gratifying focus. There's deep satisfaction with the delights and taste of food—when it's functionally eaten without guilt or overcompensation for a lack of freedom, and when the body feels absolutely no symptoms of discomfort from fullness.

For this reason, I suggest people seek out vulnerability and emotional tests of independence. I encourage people to learn how to eat based on the biological rhythms of hunger at restaurants, parties, and every social occasion possible to gain social confidence while surrounded by food and people eating and talking about dieting. It gives them a chance to retrain and recondition their habits, so dieting and overeating is not the center of their life, entertainment, emotions, or their happiness. And as they develop internal competence in themselves, regardless of the environment around them, the less likely they will ever need a diet again.

The Hunger Scale Diet

The approach and purpose behind the hunger and fullness scale can either be to continue the weight-loss battle and the vicious all-or-nothing cycle between dieting and overeating, or end it completely. If approached with the intent to end dieting and emotional eating, then there's tolerance for discomfort as the body directs you how to eat through hunger and fullness, and as old patterns of insecurity are independently secured. On the other hand, if the focus is on how much weight is lost, the hunger and fullness scale will be another set of rules, a daily battle with the scale, continued punishment for having to restrict, and the constant fear that weight will be regained.

No matter how freeing eating to the biological rhythms of hunger is, it is your choice to follow it regardless of your size and weight. The Mind:Body Method holds participants accountable for a source of motivation that is not limited by a fleeting resolve for weight reduction. It exposes dysfunctional dieting, eating, and other compensations for insecurity, giving merit to authentic and genuine emotional strength. This process gives you an opportunity to break away from the codependent cycle between dieting and emotional eating, and freedom from the emotional limitations of both. The result is emotional strength and a body set free from the torments of overeating and dieting abuse.

When Are You Ready for Dr. Simeons' HCG Protocol?

You might be ready for the hCG protocol when:

- You are indifferent about your body shape and size, if it naturally gains weight, if it naturally loses weight, if it regains weight after losing weight.
- If you are unmoved and not affected when people notice your body gaining or losing weight, and if they make assumptions or comment one way or the other.
- You can continue to be uninterested and detached from your body shape and size as you eat based on the biological rhythms of hunger and fullness.
- You don't feel entitled to a body image reward when you choose to refrain from emotional eating as insecurities and realities that are challenging arise.
- If you can accept weight gain after weight loss, while eating to the biological rhythms of hunger and fullness as you increase food options during each progressive phase after the very low-calorie protocol.
- You can respect the very low-calorie protocol as a temporary process and medical treatment that should be taken seriously. It might allow the body to heal from possible hormonal imbalances and other chronic physical issues. There are no guarantees, and even when symptoms are successfully and permanently healed, fat loss might only be temporary.
- You don't believe in thin supremacy, and don't internalize fat loss as a superior symbol of quality; then you might be emotionally ready to do the hCG protocol with less risk of

triggering urges to overeat before, during, and after the treatment.

Before you even consider the protocol as a curative physical treatment, recognize the risks that come with radical restrictions of the 500-calorie protocol. It is extreme, it is difficult, and it needs to be taken seriously. So if and when you struggle before, during, and after the process, you'll need to have compassion for yourself. You need to give yourself the grace to forgive not only what you don't recognize within yourself as an emotional problem, but that you are human. Also, there are certain things no amount of curative treatment can fix.

There are primitive mechanisms wired in all of us that yearn to feel connected with food, family, and with freedom in life. *The hCG protocol cannot provide any of those things.*

However, if you believe you have those connections in abundance, then the protocol will be nothing more than a medical treatment that might rehabilitate your body from limitations and ailments directly impacted by large amounts of body fat.

NOTE: If you can accept your body and the life that it provides you unconditionally, then the hCG protocol might be a treatment your body could benefit from. But there is no guarantee. There is no scientific evidence that it works. And there is no promise that when it is all said and done, you will be happy with your body or the life it gives you.

Chapter 18

Messages of Hope

"And once the storm is over, you won't remember how you made it through, how you managed to survive. You won't even be sure, whether the storm is really over. But one thing is certain. When you come out of the storm, you won't be the same person who walked in. That's what this storm's all about."
– Japanese writer, Haruki Murakami

I've compiled messages from people who've worked through the process, either working with me directly or trying to figure it out on their own by following sessions I've posted on my YouTube channel.

The goal with this chapter is to inspire hope that freedom is possible.

A 35-year-old Woman

Message: I've been overweight most of my life, starting in the third grade. I remember feeling confident at first, but after hearing comments from kids at school, I began to feel shame, and like something was "wrong" with me. My mom started going on diets with me to solve my "problem." I hid food at home and snuck cookies when no one was looking. Nothing worked for long, if it worked at all. I went to a group class for overweight kids where we had to weigh in front of everyone in this huge room, which was mortifying. When I was in high school, I got pretty thin.

I met my first husband, who always tried to monitor and control my diet and exercise, no matter how thin or heavy I was—I was never good enough. I went to counseling when we divorced, but couldn't seem to get to the heart of my eating issues. I became discouraged, and quit going.

I continued to gain weight. Two years ago, I weighed 297 pounds at my heaviest. After a heart-to-heart with my cousin where I confessed my intense, debilitating anxiety and self-loathing, she told me about Robin. I started listening to Robin's videos on YouTube, read her first book *Weight-Loss Apocalypse,* and it was like she'd somehow managed to get inside my head, see all the things I'd been thinking and feeling my whole life, and then verbalize and address them all.

I had one session with her after I'd been listening to her for over a year. At that point, I had lost some weight with the hCG protocol, but after binge eating again, I had gained almost all the weight back. I was so ashamed, but the session with Robin helped me set my perspective right again, because she helped me see how fear about weight gain strained how I felt about food, and how that triggered bingeing again. *She helped me forgive myself.*

However, I still struggled with extreme shame, depression and anxiety about my body, food, and life, until recently. One day I just reached the end of my emotional rope. I was in the shower (where all the deepest thoughts happen), and started crying and wallowing in despair. I was *so unhappy,* and was so tired of feeling that way.

And all of a sudden, it hit me. If my *beliefs* about myself were making me this miserable and unhappy, then why didn't I change them? No one was forcing me to feel or think this way about myself but ME. Beliefs aren't set in stone! They aren't hard facts, they're just things I think are true! I'd seen that I was

246

wrong about other things in my life and had changed my perspective, and therefore my beliefs, about those things, and I realized there's hope for me in this body image thing too.

I got out of the shower and stared at my naked body, poked and prodded all the parts I was disgusted by, but this time looked at them without judgment. I got dressed and journaled every single thought and excuse I could come up with to stay in the old thin-supremacy mindset. I let myself go fully into all of that without shame or judgment for the first time ever. I paid attention to myself, and respected and listened to myself.

I realized that I have a choice—I can choose to put those thin-supremacist sunglasses on every day and view myself *and everyone else* through them, and feel shame and misery and victimization. Or I can take those glasses off and see the light—see the beauty that's all around me, and the beauty that I AM, just the way I am, and be happy. I can choose to accept what is, and let go of the rest. As long as I'm breathing, there's hope, and something to be thankful for!

Thank you Robin, for helping me see that I had a choice, and could accept and take care of myself.

A 68-year-old Woman

Message: I started dieting when I was in high school like many young women, even though I was thin back then and didn't gain weight easily. I would eat the meals my mom prepared, but to keep from feeling deprived, I'd stash goodies in my room and eat after everyone went to bed.

My real problem with weight started when I turned to food to cope with a toxic marriage. For ten years, I was physically and mentally abused by my husband. I existed in a state of powerlessness and hopelessness, and I stopped caring about myself and my body. Even after we divorced, I continued to live a state of apathy and depression for years, eating food was my only source of freedom. I gained so much weight that I relied on a cane or a walker for even a short distance. I could not climb stairs, and I had difficulty completing daily tasks.

When my weight climbed over the 285-pound mark, I vowed to start taking care of myself. The main motivation behind changing my life was to be here for my grandchildren. Enough was enough! *I wanted to put myself first.* Putting others ahead of me led to depression, a sense of powerlessness, and a way of eating that was self-destructive. I was tired of remaining on the sidelines; now I wanted to participate more fully in life. I knew I would not have a perfect journey, but I vowed to start where I was and to make slow changes in my eating patterns and gradual changes in my physical activity.

Between 2012–2014, I lost over 160 pounds doing multiple rounds of Dr. Simeons' hCG protocol. I got down to 125 pounds. I stayed at the weight until I got a serious bladder infection in 2017, which started a spiral of eating again to soothe myself. I am now at 185 pounds, still a hundred pounds down. Regaining some of the weight back has been challenging, but this just means I have more internal work to do. But I know for a fact that I am recovering.

I started watching Robin on Weight-Loss Apocalypse YouTube channel about a year ago. It has been inspiring and hopeful to listen to people who have struggled like I have. It really helps to know others feel the same way. My biggest inspiration has been the knowledge Robin clearly shares about mindful eating and using the hunger and fullness scale. When it comes to food, I've learned that just because you can eat, doesn't mean you should. I tune into what my body is asking for, and allow myself to eat *without judgment,* and because of this I eat much more consciously than I had in the past. I approach food with an awareness of my senses. Most importantly, I stop eating when I am no longer hungry, before I become too full. When I know

I'm not hungry but still want to eat, I transition to another activity to help separate myself from the food (often that activity is exercising).

It feels good to care for myself and to enjoy my body. I've gone from hardly being able to walk, to now taking around 10,000 steps a day. Taking steps toward recovering myself has given me an excitement for life, and I am always looking for new adventures to make the most of each and every day.

For me, the journey has been best accomplished by buddying up, sharing knowledge, and being inspired by others. I actively challenge myself and encourage others to do the same. To be mindful when eating, to not seek perfection, and to take it one step at a time, inch by inch, bite by bite, and step by step. I believe in the quotation, "Start where you are. Use what you have. Do what you can."

Robin, thank you so much for all you do. Nobody but nobody can make it alone! I also believe that we are each capable beyond our imagination, and that we need to be compassionate toward our bodies; right where they are, even carrying excess weight.

A Woman in Her 40s

Message: I am not a current client, but we did have a consultation back in 2013, to help me work through my overeating issues so I could lose weight on the hCG protocol. Seems so freaking ridiculous now. I have been a subscriber to the Weight-Loss Apocalypse YouTube channel since then, but in fact I didn't watch any of Robin's videos for about four years. Then about two years ago, "out of the blue" (or I like to think the universe's perfect timing), one of your videos popped up in my suggested videos. I watched several, which changed my life forever.

I have spent 30 of my 46 years in yo-yo dieting hell. I became keenly aware of my physical body at about age five. I was and continued to be the shortest kid in the class. What I didn't realize until adulthood was that my child brain equated my short physical stature as being "less than," both inside and out. This is where the overachiever/perfectionist was born.

Since I could not control my height, I focused on what I could control: achievement and food. This masked my raging insecurity and disgust with my body because I had validation from getting good grades and other awards telling me I was okay.

When I went to college and gained the typical "freshman 15," and later gained more weight with the stress of a new job, I started to diet. This is where the non-stop diet-binge-diet cycle started, and my life being defined by my weight began.

Since then, I have literally been on every diet out there because they all work...for a little while. The mirage of the perfect body was always some-where in the future, telling me that my life would be better, and I'd feel good about myself when I achieved it. The problem was I never lived in the present moment. Fearful and embarrassed about attending social events, as well as going on vacation and being in the dreaded swimsuit prevented me from living and enjoying my life while in my bigger body. And eventually, the urge to eat would be too strong and I'd cave. I was miserable.

It was Robin's words from one of her YouTube sessions with another client that pulled me out of my dark night of the soul. I was on the precipice of starting *another* round of the hCG protocol after gaining back some of the weight from my most recent 65 lb. weight loss. Depressed and desperate, it was a series of questions inspired by your coaching videos that changed my life forever.

The catalyst came from Robin's core questions—and my answers:

☐ *What would you do if you could never diet again?*

A. What?!?! What would I do if I couldn't diet again?!?

Down the rabbit hole I went. Thinking and thinking and thinking...It felt freeing and liberating if I could get rid of dieting forever.

☐ *What would change if you had to accept your body, permanently, exactly how it is?*

A. I thought "How? But it is so fat and ugly and disgusting!" But then, something unexplainable happened— it was like my self-image separated from my body image... like two intertwined, knotted-up necklaces were finally free from one another. It was like I was looking at my body from the outside.

☐ *What if you were in a car accident and permanently lost the use of your legs?*

A. I would *have* to deal with it. I would eventually have to accept it. There's nothing I could do to change it, and I would have no choice. It would be awful and sad and hard and would change my life forever, making things harder to do, but ultimately, still doable. I could eventually do it...I could accept my physical body with no legs. Then...

☐ *If you could accept permanently losing the use of your legs, why couldn't you accept your body at a larger size and weight?*

A. This was the scenario that went through my head and provided God-inspired clarity: SNAP! WAKEUP!!! And just like that, it happened in an instant. My life shifted. My eyes opened. My soul (me) felt like it was released from a cage. I started crying the ugly cry, and I felt every emotion...happiness, sadness, anger, elation, and finally freedom. OMG, this is it! This is what it feels like!! UNBELIEVABLE!!! Even today, I am crying and getting goosebumps typing this. Freedom from the bondage I have been in. The war with myself was over. The 500 lb. gorilla was off my back. No need to "lose weight" anymore…I just lost the weight of the world off my shoulders.

Since that moment, I have never been the same. I've stopped dieting, loved my body just the way it is, although that doesn't mean I haven't at times thought about dieting again. I'm going through one of those times now.

I'm in a really good headspace, loving and accepting my body, working on my daily practice of meditation, yoga and keeping myself present. But then I have creeping thoughts of health concerns (Mom died from diabetes) and the big one, some physical pain in my hip which I have never had before.

Over the past few weeks, I've really contemplated the status of my recovery, and it actually started to sound like a good idea to do another round of the hCG protocol to lose some weight to relieve the pain. But then I recognize today the craziness of those thoughts, because it is a "logical" argument, but aren't they all?!?! This morning, I watched one of Robin's YouTube videos and decided to keep doing what I am doing. No diet and no protocol. I will add in more self-care activities to include more fruits and vegetables, without being tied to the outcome. Meaning, I am going to love me and my body, and accept and love me today, with the weight and the pain.

The greatest gift that this process of learning from you has given me is being in alignment and in tune with my intuition and being able to recognize the signs that I am on the right track for me. Thank you for inspiring me to go inward and trust myself. The constant dieting numbed and muted my inner guidance and intuition. That is what body image and dieting took away from me: I was depending on something outside of myself (diet rules), instead of going inward, listening to my hunger signals and trusting myself. Thanks to you, Robin, I do trust myself now.

Woman in Her 50s Struggling with Body Image and Emotional Eating

Message: If I hadn't stumbled upon your YouTube channel, I could have easily stumbled upon a diet, and I'd still be suffering in the same crazy cycle. I've learned so much from working with you, and because of that, my life has had major changes. I can say that I am much happier now that my weight doesn't define me, even though I was depressed about it for decades. I don't carry judgment about how I'm supposed to be, and the critical nature of what "beauty" is supposed to be. And I am no longer wasting time, energy, and money worrying about my weight or the food I'm eating. Thanks to your wisdom and help, I don't label food as good or bad anymore. I'm so grateful to have found you and this freedom.

Woman in Her 60s Struggling with Body Image and Emotional Eating

Message: I met Robin after someone recommended that I read her book and watch her YouTube videos. After hearing her talk to other people struggling with emotional eating, I decided I wanted her help. The work we did together was unbelievable. Robin, thank you for helping me realize my relationship with food was connected to other aspects of my life. I learned so much about myself, and it has been life changing. It has been over five years since we've worked together, and I am still free from dieting, emotional eating, and worrying about my weight.

A Woman in Her 30s

Message: I found Robin on YouTube and tried to stop bingeing with the use of the hunger and fullness scale. I continued to struggle so I decided to bite the bullet and work with Robin. I like the way she tells it like it is, doesn't placate your issues, and puts your issues in the spotlight. After the first consultation I wasn't sure I was ready to let go of wanting to be thinner. I decided to continue to work with her, and again after a few sessions, I wanted to quit because it was so hard and difficult to face letting go of all the things I wanted to achieve from losing weight. But the more I suffered bingeing and my frequent running back to diets, the more I realized what Robin was saying was the truth. Once I realized I had to let it go, I cried and cried. But it was like a light bulb that switched on, and it was easy after that. It took a good year of work with Robin before that moment happened—and it changed my life.

51-year-old woman Who Suffered from Depression and Emotional Eating

Message: When I started watching Robin's videos about a year and a half ago, I was in the throes of going on and off the hCG protocol and had lost and gained 40 pounds four times in a two-year period. Every time I stopped the protocol, I started bingeing knowing I'd re-lose the weight again. I was watching a video when Robin had a client rate how catastrophic weight gain was compared to other physical problems. She had the client assess how hard it would be to lose her legs in an accident, and then had her rate how bad she felt about her weight. This comparison made me realize how ridiculous the shame about my weight was and how unnecessary feeling bad about it was. That's when I decided to work with Robin.

I had put my entire life on hold trying to fix my weight, focusing on trying to be thinner. I declined vacations, jobs, relationships, dating, and starting businesses because I condemned myself, blaming my larger body. Working with Robin for about a year, I really learned that if I want freedom in life, I can't hide and be afraid of it anymore. And if I care about what other people think of my weight and body, I am giving them control over that freedom. It's been four years since, and I can't tell you how much this has changed everything in my life because of her wisdom and guidance. The freedom from feeling bad and from thinking about food all the time is beyond words. Because of our work together, my entire life has been set free.

I've started traveling, visiting over 20 cities, went back to school to take some classes, started dating, I am front and center in pictures now, have gone to the beach, and done so many things I thought had to wait until I was thinner. This is just incredible.

I've discovered that changing the way I feel about my body without needing my body to change, has made the greatest impact on my life of anything else I've ever done.

I give Robin all the credit. She has an incredible amount of compassion for a person, no matter how big she is and how much she struggles with body image and significant physical issues. She teaches people to honor themselves and their bodies, and not to be ashamed anymore—to start living their lives.

Weight-Loss Apocalypse-2: In Conclusion

As people use body image to fulfill an inner desire to fit in, feel worthy of love, and to secure themselves from being judged by family and friends, *they are using an outside physical solution to solve an inside psychological dilemma.* In a culture that promotes and glamourizes thin supremacy as a way to earn approval and love, it makes sense that believers would be hypercritical of their body and body fat, and would be attracted to methods to reduce their body shape and size. For this reason, hormonal therapies such as Dr. Simeons' hCG protocol are not being applied as medical treatment for the body, but are being inappropriately approached as solutions for poor body image and low self-esteem.

Unfortunately, this body-image minded approach has unintended consequences that might harm the mind and body of those attempting the protocol.

Not only can it exacerbate emotional eating problems, but it could promote a person's body to be even more sensitive to fat gain.

As an advocate of Dr. Simeons' hCG protocol, I believe the protocol has the potential to be a legitimized medical treatment. However, it isn't appropriate for all people—just because they have adequate body fat and hormonal symptoms that would justify the very-low calorie protocol. There are psychological and emotional components to body image that should be addressed and resolved prior to considering the protocol a suitable physical solution. This is true not only because physical solutions can't solve emotional problems, but because beliefs that "being thinner is better" have a direct impact on people's impulse to emotionally overeat.

As people experience shame and embarrassment about their body fat, research suggests they are more likely to eat emotionally, especially before and after a food-restrictive diet. Without addressing the underlying beliefs that impel a person to feel bad about her body, no matter how much body fat is lost during the hCG protocol, she is likely to fear food, fear her body, and have increased emotional strain eating once the protocol is over.

No matter what weight-loss method is used, unless you are willing to face the difficult reality that self-worth is formed from unconditionally accepting the truth of yourself, feelings of unworthiness and shame will continue to be there, no matter how much weight you lose.

When a body image that has dominated a person's life is surrendered, her self-worth is freed up to be intrinsically and truthfully defined. The shame that originated from thin-supremacy beliefs diminish, and so does the pressure to diet and her urge to eat emotionally.

This isn't just a weight-loss apocalypse, but it's a recovery of self-worth. It's a body-image apocalypse.

Acknowledgments

I'd like to thank all the clients I've coached over the years who were willing to share their stories to the world on my YouTube channel. You are helping others by allowing them to witness your struggles and success in the process of recovery.

Next, I'd like to acknowledge and thank my copy development and line editor, Connie Anderson of Words and Deeds, Inc. Without her talents and the integrity of her work, I would have never finished this project, and it would've been far more difficult to read. Connie has been an imperative partner in capturing for the reader what I am trying to communicate. She is incredibly gifted and has been an essential influence to this body of work. Many people had told me that I'm a good writer—but my response is to let them know I have an incredible editor.

A special thank you to Denise Watson and Dr. Ed Hagen from Vivify Integrative Health in Hudson, Wisconsin. You gave me the opportunity to teach your patients, one by one, for years. Repeating the same explanation over and over, hundreds of times, was an invaluable part of refining how I teach the protocol process to participants. This work with you has been precious.

Thank you to my professors at Boise State University. Without such rigorous educational standards, I couldn't have understood the research that provided the basis for the content discussed in this book. To the Kinesiology department: Thank you for having such passion for the health of the human mind and body.

My hard-working and humble parents—for being the ultimate examples of perseverance and integrity. To sister Becky for introducing me to the hCG protocol, listening to my ignorant and skeptical rant, and then forgiving me. To sister Katie for your incredible artistic mind, and for the book title and cover design. To them and all my other siblings—Steve, Laura, Daniel, Jennalee, Debbie, Melissa, Cliff, Mike, Big Jeff, Little Jeff, and Jean—for helping develop my "character."

References

(1.) Engeln-Maddox, R. (2005). Cognitive responses to idealized media images of women: The relationship of social comparison and critical processing to body image disturbance in college women. *Journal of Social and Clinical Psychology.* 24(8), 1114-1138. https://doi.org/10.1521/jscp.2005.24.8.1114

(2.) Dittmar, Helga (2007). The Costs of Consumer Culture and the "Cage Within": The Impact of the Material "Good Life" and "Body Perfect" Ideals on Individuals" *Identity and Well-Being, Psychological Inquiry.* 18(1), 23-31, doi: 10.1080/10478400701389045

(3.) Hesse-Biber, S., Leavy, P., Quinn, C.E., Zoino, J. (2006). The mass marketing of disordered eating and Eating Disorders: The social psychology of women, thinness and culture. *Women's Studies International Forum.* 29: 208-224. doi: 10.1016/j.wsif.2006.03.007

(4.) Arjan E. R. Bos., John B. Pryor., Glenn D. Reeder & Sarah E. Stutterheim. (2013). Stigma: Advances in Theory and Research. *Basic and Applied Social Psychology.* 35(1), 1-9. http://dx.doi.org/10.1080/01973533.2012.746147

(5.) Andreyeva, T., Puhl, R. M. and Brownell, K. D. (2008). Changes in Perceived Weight Discrimination Among Americans, 1995–1996 Through 2004–2006. *Obesity*. 16: 1129-1134. doi:10.1038/oby.2008.35

(6.) Puhl, R. M. and Brownell, K. D. (2006). Confronting and Coping with Weight Stigma: An Investigation of Overweight and Obese Adults. *Obesity*. 14: 1802-1815. doi:10.1038/oby.2006.208

(7.) Stone, O., & Werner, P. (2012). Israeli Dietitians' Professional Stigma Attached to Obese Patients. *Qualitative Health Research*. 22(6), 768–76. https://doi.org/10.1177/1049732311431942

(8.) Edelstein, Sari PhD, RD; Silva, Nicole MS, RD; Mancini, Lisa BS. (2009). Obesity Bias Among Dietitians by Using the Fat People-Thin People Implicit Association Test. *Topics in Clinical Nutrition*. 24 (1), 67–72. doi: 0.1097/TIN.0b013e3181989af1

(9.) Phelan, S. M., Burgess, D. J., Yeazel, M. W., Hellerstedt, W. L., Griffin, J. M., & van Ryn, M. (2015). Impact of weight bias and stigma on quality of care and outcomes for patients with obesity. *Obesity Reviews: an official journal of the International Association for the Study of Obesity*. 16 (4), 319–326. doi:10.1111/obr.12266

(10.)Geraldine M. Budd, Megan Mariotti, Diane Graff, Kathleen Falkenstein. (2011). Health care professionals' attitudes about obesity: An integrative review, *Applied Nursing Research*. 24 (3), 127-137. https://doi.org/10.1016/j.apnr.2009.05.001

(11.) Phelan, S. M., Burgess, D. J., Yeazel, M. W., Hellerstedt, W. L., Griffin, J. M., & van Ryn, M. (2015). Impact of weight bias and stigma on quality of care and outcomes for patients with obesity. *Obesity Reviews: an official journal of the International Association for the Study of Obesity.* 16(4), 319–326. doi:10.1111/obr.12266

(12.) Bertakis, K. D. and Azari, R. (2005). The Impact of Obesity on Primary Care Visits. *Obesity Research.* 13: 1615-1623. doi:10.1038/oby.2005.198

(13.) Aldrich, Tess & Hackley, Barbara. (2010). The Impact of Obesity on Gynecologic Cancer Screening: An Integrative Literature Review. *Journal of Midwifery & Women's Health.* 55: 344-56. doi: 10.1016/j.jmwh.2009.10.001

(14.) Satter, Ellyn. (2007). Eating competence: definition and evidence for the Satter Eating Competence model. *Journal of Nutrition Education Behavior.* Sep-Oct;39(5):S142-53 doi:10.1016/j.jneb.2007.01.006

(15.) Wilke, Joy. (2014). Nearly half in U.S. remain worried about their weight. *Gallup.* https://news.gallup.com/poll/174089/nearly-half-remain-worried-weight.aspx

(16.) Carr, K. D. (2011). Food scarcity, neuroadaptations, and the pathogenic potential of dieting in an unnatural ecology: binge eating and drug abuse. *Physiology & Behavior.* 104(1), 162–167. doi:10.1016/j.physbeh.2011.04.023

(17.) Hill, Andrew. (2007). The Psychology of Food Cravings. *The Proceedings of the Nutrition Society.* 66: 277-285. doi:10.1017/S0029665107005502.

(18.) Seacat, J. D. & Mickelson, K. D. (2009). Stereotype Threat and the Exercise/ Dietary Health Intentions of Overweight Women. *Journal of Health Psychology.* 14(4), 556–567. https://doi.org/10.1177/1359105309103575

(19.) Luchetti, M., Barkley, J. M., Stephan, Y., Terracciano, A., & Sutin, A. R. (2014). Five-factor model personality traits and in-flammatory markers: new data and a meta-analysis. *Psychoneu-roendocrinology.* 50: 181–193. doi:10.1016/j.psyneuen.2014.08.014

(20.) Pearl, Rebecca & Puhl, Rebecca. (2016). The distinct effects of internalizing weight bias: An experimental study. *Body Image.* 17: 38-42. doi:10.1016/j.bodyim.2016.02.002

(21.) Ying-Hsien Chao, Chao-Chin Yang, Wen-Bin Chiou. (2012) Food as ego-protective remedy for people experiencing shame. Experimental evidence for a new perspective on weight-related shame. *Appetite.* 59(2), 570-575. https://doi.org/10.1016/j.appet.2012.07.007

(22.) Hawkins, David.R. (2018) *Map of Consciousness. Book of Slides (The Complete Collection Presented at the 2002-2011 Lectures with Clarifications.* Pages 12,104-107

(23.) M. Macht and G. Simons. (2000). Emotions and Eating in Everyday Life. *Appetite.* 35(1), 65-71. doi:10.1006/appe.2000.0325

(24.) Puhl, R. M. and Heuer, C. A. (2009), The Stigma of Obesity: A Review and Update. *Obesity.* 17: 941-964. doi:10.1038/oby.2008.636

(25.) Major, Brenda, Hunger, Jeffrey M., Bunyan, Debra P., Miller, Carol T. (2014). The ironic effects of weight stigma. *Journal of Experimental Social Psychology.* 51: Pages 74-80, https://doi.org/10.1016/j.jesp.2013.11.009.

(26.) Sickel, A., Seacat, J., Nabors, Nina. (2014). Mental health stigma update: A review of consequences. *Advances in Mental Health.* 12: 202-215. doi:10.1080/18374905.2014.11081898.

(27.) Pearl, R. L., White, M. A., & Grilo, C. M. (2014). Overvaluation of shape and weight as a mediator between self-esteem and weight bias internalization among patients with binge eating disorder. *Eating Behaviors.* 15(2), 259–261. doi:10.1016/j.eatbeh.2014.03.005

(28.) Aubie, C. D., & Jarry, J. L. (2009). Weight-related teasing increases eating in binge eaters. *Journal of Social and Clinical Psychology.* 28(7), 909-936. https://doi.org/10.1016/j.eatbeh.2013.06.012.

(29.) Carels, et al. (2009). Internalized weight stigma and its ideological correlates among weight loss treatment seeking adults. *Eating and Weight Disorders.* 14(2-3):e92-e97. doi:10.1007/bf03327805

(30.) Sutin, A. R., Stephan, Y., Luchetti, M. and Terracciano, A. (2014). Perceived weight discrimination and C–reactive protein. *Obesity.* 22: 1959-1961. doi:10.1002/oby.20789

(31.) Schvey, N. A., Puhl, R. M. and Brownell, K. D. (2011). The Impact of Weight Stigma on Caloric Consumption. *Obesity*. 19: 1957-1962. doi:10.1038/oby.2011.204

(32.) Schvey, Natasha & Puhl, Rebecca & Brownell, Kelly. (2014). The Stress of Stigma: Exploring the Effect of Weight Stigma on Cortisol Reactivity. *Psychosomatic Medicine*. 76. doi:10.1097/PSY.0000000000000031.

(33.) Schwimmer, JB., et al. (2003). Obesity, insulin resistance, and other clinicopathological correlates of pediatric nonalcoholic fatty liver disease. *The Journal of Pediatrics*. 143:500–505.

(34.) Sutin, A. R., Stephan, Y., & Terracciano, A. (2015). Weight Discrimination and Risk of Mortality. *Psychological Science*. 26(11), 1803–811. https://doi.org/10.1177/0956797615601103

(35.) Sutin, AR., Zonderman, AB., Ferrucci L., Terracciano A. (2013). Personality traits and chronic disease: implications for adult personality development. *The Journals of Gerontology: Series B, Psychological Sciences and Social Sciences*. 68(6):912-20.

SECOND
EDITION

BOOK 1

WEIGHT-

EMOTIONAL EATING

LOSS

REHAB THROUGH

APOCALYPSE

THE HCG PROTOCOL

ROBIN PHIPPS WOODALL

AVAILABLE NOW!

After 8 years, author Robin Phipps Woodall has updated *Weight-Loss Apocalypse*, adding 52 pages of new mind-opening content. In the second edition, along with the important discussions of Dr. Simeons' hCG protocol, the need for further scientific investigation, and the hunger and fullness scale, Robin examines further the impact dieting has on emotional eating.

She explains: Until the influence that dieting has on over-eating or emotional eating is exposed as problematic, the demand for excessive amounts of food will continue, and weight gain will always be viewed as the problem. This additional discussion is instrumental in preparing the reader for the next book in the series: *Weight-Loss Apocalypse, Book 2*, which complements this book by addressing how body image negatively impacts how people approach Dr. Simeons' protocol.

For this reason, Robin is excited to present this updated second edition as *Weight-Loss Apocalypse, Book 1*.

End life-crippling diet obsession and binge eating for good

Although you can't imagine a way to escape,

PERMANENT RECOVERY IS POSSIBLE.

REQUEST TO WORK WITH ROBIN NOW

READ ROBIN'S STORY

MORE INFORMATION

WEIGHT-LOSS APOCALYPSE

FOR MORE INFORMATION

Visit our website:
https://weightlossapocalypse.com

WeightLossApocalypse
4.68K subscribers   ⚙️

4:56

SECOND EDITION OF WEIGHT-LOSS APOCALYPSE AVAILABLE NOW!
WeightLossApocalypse · 152 views
1 week ago

Uploads

SECOND EDITION

FOR MORE INFORMATION

Follow on YouTube:
https://youtube.com/user/weightlossapocalypse

Website:
https://weightlossapocalypse.com

Email:
info@mindbodyhcg.com

YouTube:
https://youtube.com/user/weightlossapocalypse

Instagram:
@WeightLossApocalypse

Twitter:
@MindBodyMethod

Facebook:
Weight-Loss Apocalypse

Made in the USA
Monee, IL
23 June 2021